THE ESSENTIAL GUIDE TO
HEALTH ANXIETY

Dennis Simsek

Note to the Reader: The content in this book is for informational purposes only and must not be regarded as medical advice. No action or inaction should be taken merely on the content of this information; instead, readers should consult appropriate health professionals on any matter relating to their health and well-being.

Table of Contents

Foreword

My name is Dennis Simsek and I am healed from health anxiety. I know that may sound impossible to those who are currently suffering, but I assure you, overcoming health anxiety is possible for everyone, even you. Within the contents of this book, I have outlined all the understandings, inspirations, tools, and a series of relatable stories that you need to achieve the mental health stability you deserve. Because a life filled with health anxiety is no life at all, and if you're reading this book it's because you have decided that managing your symptoms forever is just not an option for you.

I've written this book for anyone going through health anxiety who has reached the point of 'no return.' A place of such deep emotional dissatisfaction around living a life filled with irrational fear and worry. Why should you care about what I have to say? Because while most people in your life will not truly understand what it is you're currently going through, I do.

I understand what it's like to have the people around you not understand your health anxiety. I understand the frustrations around the inability to find a long-term solution to the inner conflicts. I've been where you are. I've experienced a state of unrelenting mental chatter and bodily symptoms that simply won't let up no matter where you are and what you do. The road toward betterment is an

1

unrelenting experience, though it is one that is highly satisfying, at least once progress begins to be made.

I've been there. And now I am here for you.

Introduction

Health anxiety is like battling a professional chess player. It always seems like he (or she) is 4 or 5 steps ahead of you no matter what mental or behavioral tricks you pull on it. Worse, your health anxiety is like a chess player that doesn't necessarily want to win but would prefer to hold on to your harmful interpretations about yourself and cast reality out. "Protect me less," I remember crying out during my years with health anxiety, but, like an over-protective mother helicoptering around us at every turn (bless them), it would not let up.

Health anxiety can make a sane person feel insane, a healthy person feel sick, and a loved person feel unloved.

Today, a large portion of the world lives in the shadows of health anxiety. I decided to create this essential guide to help people understand and address this widespread issue, commonly known as hypochondria. In this book, you will find yourself nodding your head in approval as you run into very relatable content and stories that I present. You'll encounter new approaches to healing health anxiety that will help move you out of the repeating cycle of babysitting your anxiety symptoms and falling victim to certain unhelpful ideas.

Health anxiety is meant to be a stepping stone, not an identity. Your body uses it to learn the lessons needed in order to apply them to the different aspects of your life. While healing, you will once again consciously begin to experience the world through your senses rather than unconsciously reacting to the interpretation made by your subconscious mind based on your past. Remember, nothing will change until we can bring to our conscious awareness what we've been unaware of for some time, and health anxiety is no different.

With hypochondria, the pain and suffering we experience are closely linked to our inability to connect our heartfelt feelings and beliefs with our own conscious perceptions. This includes the anxiety symptoms. The feelings of doom that accompany the anxiety symptoms spur on a terrorizing idea of ill health which, over time, if coupled with stronger emotions, we believe are real symptoms of illness. Within a short period of time we find ourselves negatively internal rather than emotionally neutral or positively internal, which takes our focus completely off the present moment.

To be negatively internal is to live by what I call the 'standing guard' rule. The standing guard rule demands that we identify the threat in all things (especially our bodily symptoms and sensations) before any other assumptions are made. So, we stand guard to external things like new experiences, friends we're about to meet, the waves crashing on the ocean, and even the birds singing high up on a tree (it's possible they could swoop down and take out an eye, you know). We continue to stand guard internally, thinking that a lump in the throat feeling is throat cancer, a headache is a brain tumour, and involuntary twitching could potentially mean ALS. It's hard work maintaining health anxiety. I can tell you that much because all of our focus and energy is spent on survival and not experiencing the present itself. I have a word for this kind of daily cycle, I call it 'preventititis.' To look to constantly prevent the worst, in turn we experience the illusion of having control over everything while moving further away from trusting in the unfolding of this life.

If we are always in survival mode, our mind, body, and spirit never get the chance to see things as they really are. Rather, they see them as what they could potentially and catastrophically be.

To a system so highly dedicated to survival (this includes the survival of your social status, not only your physical health), our batteries never seem to recharge. The further depleted we are, the more active our amygdala becomes (the processing center for our emotions and memories associated with fear). We continue to feel drained even after a nap or an 8-hour good night's sleep, waking up exhausted and pessimistic about the upcoming day. If any of this sounds remotely like you or someone you know, I'm glad you picked up this essential guide to health anxiety. Because my only goal in this introduction is to make sure you don't feel alone anymore, that you no longer feel like you must do this by yourself. There will, of course, come a time when you'll have to spread your wings and use the knowledge and tools from this book to overcome your inner blocks, but for now, we will walk hand in hand up the steps of the health anxiety healing ladder together.

Up to the time of writing this book I've coached over 15,000 people worldwide on their journey to health anxiety freedom through private 1-on-1 sessions, online coaching programs, workshops, masterclasses, and more. You can rest assured that the knowledge and wisdom that will guide you through this book has been tried and tested. I like to refer to the healing process as a ladder system, and the only way to get to the next step is to learn and apply what you need to in the present step. This book is created in a very progressive manner in that it identifies the common experiences health anxiety sufferers go through and guides you from one step on the ladder to the next. Sometimes this means deeper reflection, a change in behavior at a certain point in the day, or even the act of inaction in moments when you normally feel like something must be done. As we go forward, you will need to trust the intuition that has been taken over by a critical mind that believes it has all the answers. Your intuition is your heart sense, your playful side, your lighter side. It is the side of you that you lost touch with early on in your life due to the personal and generational traumas you may have experienced.

When I refer to trauma in this book, I'm not referring to a life-threatening or highly dangerous scenario. But rather, I'm referring to an experience that your subconscious mind (inner child) created false and lasting beliefs around. This could be as simple as having your toy taken away from you while you were in the bath as a child. The connection that formed at that very moment was possibly: 'Don't have fun, don't be spontaneous, because the experience is fleeting and will be taken from you anyway.' How does this connect to health anxiety today, you may ask? It is the accumulation of such experiences that led to the core beliefs you hold in your subconscious mind today. They revolve around fear, as true and unconditional love became suppressed more deeply. As cliché as it sounds, love really is the antidote to healing health anxiety for good. To give you an example of this from my own life, I absolutely hated the dizziness that was at the forefront of my days with health anxiety. That is, until I realized why it was there. I realized it was my body chemically protecting me from future scenarios of overwhelm. It was in those very moments that I stopped having panic attacks and stopped carrying the label of panic disorder around, as the dizziness was the protection from panic. Now that is true love. So instead of berating my dizziness, I thanked it. I blessed it and moved with it rather than look to escape it. I learned that to escape an anxiety symptom is nearly impossible, but that working with it conserves your energy reserves so that you can use it towards your healing.

I've realized after all this time spent helping health anxiety sufferers to heal, all I was really doing was teaching them to understand the different ways in which their inner child developed traumatic messages,

and relayed these messages to the conscious mind in the form of bodily symptoms later on in life.

To stay on the topic of the health anxiety symptom commonly known as dizziness for a moment, I realized after some time that every time my attention turned to it, I was mentally neutral towards it. Could mental and emotional neutrality towards our symptoms and intrusive thoughts be the key to healing health anxiety? I believe it's an important component, yes. But this kind of acceptance means that you must build up a new relationship with your body whether it 'feels right' or not. Healing health anxiety is all about relationship building, and the most important relationships you must build are with the things you fear and are avoiding the most. For example, for a long time I couldn't utter the word 'cancer' or hear it from anyone else, or I would internalize it and be taken down a spiral of panic and health anxiety. But there came a time when the word became benign to me, and I could throw it around loosely, which led me to detaching one person's life journey from my own. Once this hits you at an emotional level rather than being just a nice idea, you're going to find yourself in uncharted territory. This is when we can start to truly build ourselves back up again from the bottom up. No longer are we so addicted to the stress chemicals that make us believe we can't live without them. Instead, we see how a life of inner peace is, in fact, deserved, and that we are more than capable of meeting with it daily.

Every step up this health anxiety healing ladder will demand something new from you.

It's important to make note of this now, for as we progress we may hit a plateau. For example, we may begin to fear our physical symptoms less and less or even not at all anymore, but occasionally still feel depressed and confused about life. This step could very well signify a grey area and reflect a re-building phase where you get to choose how you think, what you do, and who you are (we'll dive deeper into this later on in the book). If you're stuck on this step, it may signify a fear of creating since you've lived in suppression for so long that you no longer believe you are capable of creating a new you, or even tapping into the different parts of you that you've neglected for so long. There can be some degree of hesitation with anything new you encounter and there can be a sense of uncertainty as well, and these are both good signs, signs of progress. There is not one person on this planet that is completely fearless. Everyone fears something at a conscious and subconscious level. As a health anxiety sufferer, you fear what it would be like and whether you will be fully accepted by others to live as you truly want to. Many people think it is the fear of death that perpetuates health anxiety, but I believe that that is just a cover-up to the fear of revealing our true identities and living life to the fullest. This is where making peace with the unknown becomes so critical.

Fear not what the future holds, my friend, since the future is yet not here. Our immediate concern is this: who do you need to be right at this moment to keep up with the healing process? Who do you need to be while reading this book to get the most out of it and affect your life positively? If you read this book the same way you read your last book, will you be on your way to healing your health anxiety? Possibly, possibly not, since maybe your heart wasn't into the last book that you 'tried' to read. This isn't like that book; this book needs to be studied like your life depends on it, or else everything will just pass you by and the only thing you'll feel at the end is regret. Stop, think, reread, reflect, heal.

Become the contents of this book and you will reach your goal of healing health anxiety.

Have patience as you read, since patience reflects self-love. As much as we'd like to turn a switch and be done with health anxiety, that's rarely the case. Plug away and enjoy each chapter on the ladder towards healing. At times you will feel you need to put down the book when you need to, and at times you will want to reread a chapter. Remember, have patience. There is a glossary on the last few pages that you can reference to remind yourself of the terms I use. Your happiness will be a result of your commitment and patience with the process, so there's no need to make happiness your goal. Healing health anxiety is leaving the fear-based trance you're currently living in for good. This trance denies the existence of inner peace since inner peace leads to being content, and our survival instincts know that there is no action being taken when we are content. There is only seeing, hearing, feeling, smelling, tasting, and sensing without judgment, without problem-solving. This is where you will get to soon enough, I truly believe this, so stay strong and enjoy the journey.

Chapter 1:
The Realization & Recognition of Health Anxiety

The process of truly learning while healing begins with the recognition that we are hypochondriacs. Often this pattern is coupled with panic attacks or generalized anxiety that makes functioning within society that much more challenging. Most health anxiety sufferers won't admit that this is the cause of their suffering until every physical test under the sun has been made. The idea that this suffering could be the result of a highly sensitized bodily intelligence that picks up on unconscious triggers within an environment (present or future) isn't something we really consider or accept until later on in the journey, once we've finally concluded that our suffering could, in fact, be emotionally caused. The body will react anxiously way before the conscious mind even knows what is going on. The conscious mind is often the last to know what's really going on, and more often than not (within the context of health anxiety) tags along to the survival and emotional parts of our brain, spurring on more anxiousness.

Like a dog chasing its tail, health anxiety sufferers chase a disease or illness that simply does not exist.

While at the doctor's office, the doctor may provide nine pieces of information that connect to good physical health and 1 vague piece of 'cautious' information that causes a world of 'what if's' to open up in our minds. We forget the nine positive pieces of information and instead hyper-focus on the one negative piece that confirms in our minds the gloomy spiral we seem to be heading toward. This is how self-debilitating patterns get formed and make us believe that something that isn't real for us really is, or could be soon enough. How do we let something like this happen? Why can't we simply be content with the nine pieces of information that confirm our optimal physical health? Because our internal systems want to maintain whatever emotional state we find ourselves in most often.

The emotional refractory period, a system within us dedicated to sorting for and distorting information within our environment, looks for familiarity. So, if fear is the leading emotion for the majority of the day (and most of our lives) it will look for it and even distort the information we perceive to continue along the path of fear. Our subconscious minds don't like change much. It likes consistency, even when it causes us pain. When it comes to health anxiety the problem isn't necessarily the difficulty in healing health anxiety, but rather it is convincing our subconscious minds that change is safe, necessary, and reliable. This is where the way you communicate with your inner child becomes vital, as the level of emotional intensity during your inner dialogues and your changes in behavior will ultimately be the deciding factor to whether a perception of fear changes to safety. It is also vitally important that once you've received a diagnosis that connects you to anxiety, you don't slap it on your forehead for everyone to see. You are not a victim here; you're simply dealing with patterns and habits that feel so automatic that we've convinced ourselves that they are a part of who we are. When, in reality, they are just a bundle of habits. Some of the negative habits that spur on health anxiety can be boiled down to:

Unconscious imagery-based habits: Waking up and predicting through inner pictures and movies how debilitating the day will be due to the anxiety symptoms and thought patterns we'll have to grapple with. We may not be conscious of these mental movies and slideshows that we run in our minds, but when feelings get connected to thought, we begin to imagine a future based on similarities in our past and halt the process of creating a future based on our desires. Therefore, it's vitally important that we learn to consciously run internal movies of what we *want* to see happen rather than unconsciously run internal movies of what we *don't* want to happen. The best time to do this is within the first 20 minutes of waking up and in the last 20 minutes prior to sleep, as this is when our mental states allow us to have direct access to the subconscious mind's storage system. The critical faculty (the security guard at the doorway of your mind protecting your fear-based perceptions and beliefs) is bypassed during these two time periods. This means that upon waking up and going to sleep, if you can tap into imagery that spur on a deep feeling of progress, optimal health, and empowerment before it takes place in the future, you have planted a seed in the soil of your own subconscious mind which will bloom as your future actions match the imagery.

If someone asked me what was the single most powerful tool that took me out of health anxiety and into inner peace, I would say incorporating transformative mental movies while still feeling under a mild trance state within these 2 separate times of the day is key. To try this yourself, go to The Anxiety Guy YouTube channel and look up the 'Reframing' playlist to be guided through the process, or you may begin one of my digital programs at www.theanxietyguy.com.

Mental habits: When it comes to the mental realm there's a difference between replaying and thinking. Most people believe they are thinking as they go through the day when in fact they're just replaying. Replaying is adopting the same ideas around a similar context day after day. It's like a record player that plays the same record each day, and what happens if you play the same song consistently? You'll experience the same feelings you always have. Change to a different record and suddenly you will be thinking. This will push you out of your mental comfort zones and into a place of curious vulnerability. Although the new feeling connected to the new record (thought) may feel different, different in your world must be associated with safety rather than danger. Different is good. We must make that different feeling the new normal for you in order to heal health anxiety for good. Ideas are just that, ideas. Nothing more and nothing less. It is not the mental ideas that ruin us or lift us up, it's what we do during the moments we first become aware of them. Leaving an idea alone makes it lose its power over us, and so does replacing one idea with a new one (when coupled with emotion and decisiveness). The act of adding feeling, words, and even physical action to an idea will make it more real in our bodies, which in turn will potentially spur on the stress chemicals that make us think that we are always in danger. This is the opportunity we need to rewire our subconscious reaction in a positive way. Ask yourself this: for the greater part of your day are you replaying old ideas or creating new ones? You have more options on how to perceive something than you may think, and starting today you get to believe whatever you want to believe about your body signals, yourself, the world, unfamiliar experiences, everything. So, believe in change and have faith that these new ideas about your health and the safety of this world and you can and will turn these new ideas into firmed-up beliefs.

Verbal habits: What we say cements our beliefs and identity, literally, words are commands. Words hold a tremendous power to encourage change or to leave us feeling victimized. More often than not, when we speak to others in a victim-like manner due to our health anxiety, we're actually just looking to gain something from the other person, even if this is not our conscious intention. These are called secondary gains. Consciously, it's a crazy idea to live in misery in the hopes of receiving acceptance, connection, and love from another person. But, unfortunately, we aren't conscious enough of the day to realize what it is we are doing and why we are doing it.

When I work with someone personally, one of the first places I look to begin the healing process with them is their secondary gains. I then help them to understand that whatever they didn't receive as a child they may be unconsciously looking to receive through victimhood. This is happening below the level of conscious awareness as mentioned, a need that is being fulfilled which leads us to the purpose for keeping anxiety close by at all times. When it comes to your verbal communication with others however, it's difficult to completely stop saying things that spur on health anxiety. It is much easier to replace these words with new words. A few words you must replace starting today are:

Trying. Instead of using 'trying' in a sentence like, 'I'm trying my best', use the word 'learning.' For instance, 'I'm now learning what works and what doesn't for me'. The word trying literally means failing, which your inner child would prefer you to use consistently so that the idea of change doesn't become something you commit to for too long. Trying isn't committing, and committing could change all that the subconscious mind believes is best for you. As we go through this book, you'll begin to recognize within you the vast number of defense mechanisms the subconscious mind uses to keep things as they are, even if that means continued suffering, since familiarity equals safety.

How. People use the word 'how' to justify not knowing what to do to heal when in fact, they simply don't trust deeply enough in what they already know. Health anxiety, at its core, is a lack of trust in the uncertain and a deep desire to maintain control over a life that has felt out of control for the most part. Health anxiety healing is driven by a reconnection with our 'higher selves' and trust, trusting in a direction that feels unfamiliar and vulnerable to us. When someone asks 'how do I heal that one lingering anxiety symptom?' what they're really saying is 'I'm afraid to be courageous enough to believe in a new idea and action that is brought on by my higher self, so I'll stay in a state of confusion instead'. This state of confusion is a place that is familiar and reliable to a health anxiety sufferer in that they feel like it won't get any worse than it is already. They know what to expect from one day to the next in terms of how they'll feel. However, if things start to change, they unconsciously feel like their world may spiral uncontrollably and they won't be able to handle it. The easiest way out of constantly using the word how, as in 'how can I do something', is to simply look at what doesn't work. Look back on your worst health anxiety days recently. What sort of habits did you engage in upon waking up, showering, driving to work, conversing with others, while having dinner, prior to bed, etc. As you bring your subconsciously led daily habits into conscious awareness you will find hidden perceptions, reactions, and even core beliefs that tend to spur on further health anxiety. Starting today, make sure to pay more attention to what's taking place in your inner world (curiosity over franticness) as you take a leap of faith into a world of trusting what you already know enough to courageously act on it consistently. And always remember, if confusion continues to present itself, the most straightforward path to freedom from health anxiety is to recognize what doesn't work.

Always. Health anxiety sufferers over-use the word 'always' to convince themselves that the same experience happens to them repeatedly, when in reality most of the time it only happens sporadically. A good example of this is 'I always feel the same lump in the throat feeling when I'm at work'. I wouldn't be so sure about that though, since the throat is our avenue of expression (we'll be going deeper into the true suppressed and emotionally led meanings behind your symptoms in later chapters) and you may be feeling this lump sensation around one particular person, or when your workload gets too heavy, or during a meeting. For most of us, this inability to express emotions trickles down from childhood when a certain authority figure made us feel smaller than small. We couldn't express our thoughts and needs then, and our bodily response was this lump sensation, so now, as adults, anything that triggers the subconscious mind in a similar fashion will spur on the same sensation of restriction or a lump feeling in the throat. It's the inability to freely and openly express our thoughts and feelings that have led to the suppression that we feel in certain aspects of our bodies that we know very well as being our anxiety symptoms. This suppression was so that we followed the lead of our authority figures, didn't disappoint anyone out of fear of a conflict occurring, and our lack of belief in our own capabilities.

Instead of using the word 'always', learn to replace it with 'sometimes'. I sometimes feel this physical symptom of anxiety during this experience. Now we are moving away from generalizing and moving toward flexibility in perception. We are led to use similar words from one day to the next in order to stay in tune with the fear led identity we've grown accustomed to all these years. Change your words, and you will meet with an unfamiliar feeling. That very feeling when trusted and built upon will lead to transformation.

Behavioral habits: Behaviors are the foundations of our identity. What we do and don't do from moment to moment dictates what we believe about ourselves and the world. Act like a health anxiety sufferer and all that comes with it will be yours. This doesn't mean you must 'fake it till you make it,' since the mindset of faking it will lead to never owning what it is you are doing. Rather, I'd like you to see yourself as a bundle of 'persona parts'. There are parts to you that are genuinely connected to fear and parts of you that are genuinely connected to love. Your fear-based parts have been taking over your persona for some time now and your loving parts have been neglected. For example, when you wake up and look in the mirror you probably see someone who is a victim of their inner circumstances. This would be to follow the lead of your fear-centered persona parts. However, the moment you catch yourself about to go down this familiar path, stop and listen to your loving and encouraging parts instead. You will begin the process of replacing the old outdated beliefs you have about yourself. Changing behaviors can be intimidating at first, so it's best to focus on listening to the positive parts of you that you've neglected and let them lead you toward what action is best in any given moment. Some of these parts can be connected to:

- Patience
- Optimism
- Humor
- Being content
- Creativity
- Wonder
- Playfulness
- Laughter

These are just a few examples of your loving 'persona parts'. Remember, if it feels like an unfamiliar behavior, it's most likely the one that will help you to grow into your true divine, loving and peaceful higher self. Is today the day you place a higher priority, and therefore energy, on bringing out your loving persona parts while simultaneously turning down the volume of your fear-centered parts? I sure hope so, since the simple recognition of the fact that you've been prioritizing your fear-centered persona parts more than your loving persona parts is enough to 'get the wheels turning', so to speak. So much of healing health anxiety for good is giving ourselves the permission to believe in and be someone different. Once you feel yourself beginning to step over this hurdle, you are on your way to trusting in a physical body that is capable of healing pretty much anything, and a mind that is capable of perceiving things as they are, not worse than what they are.

Physiological habits. These are the habits that pertain to your body and how you use them from one moment to the next. For example, health anxiety sufferers are chronic shallow breathers, which creates a tunnel vision effect that allows us to only focus on threats and limitations. Expanded and diaphragmatic breathing, on the other hand, increases the flexibility in our thinking and calms our nervous system enough to bring about a genuine sense of inner peace. For someone going through health anxiety, the most effective way to breathe throughout the day is 'slow and steady', which simply translates into slow and consistent inhales and exhales through the belly. I suggest focusing on a continuous 4-second inhale followed by a 4-second exhale until your unconscious mind can take over this breathing rhythm. Begin implementing the words 'slow and steady' together with this breathing pattern not only when things get overwhelming, but also throughout the entire day, even when you are feeling neutral rather than in a heightened or sensitized emotional state. This is a great habit to begin building and will create a domino effect that will affect the way you perceive threats, how you respond to them, and how you imagine your future self interacting with the world. Your pace also plays a leading role in terms of which emotions you default to most often. If you wake up and speed through your daily to-do's, you are more vulnerable to feelings and ideas around ill health. However, if you slow down your pace as you speak, walk, drive, work, eat, etc., you will fortify yourself to those same ideas and feelings and soon you'll become increasingly disinterested by them.

Disinterest and boredom around irrational fear leads to freedom from health anxiety.

The recognition of being a health anxiety sufferer is the beginning of the end of a life lived within the shadows of fear and anxiety. This moment presents the opportunity to begin re-inventing yourself rather than continuing to live a lie for the sake of familiarity. It's not a moment you should be afraid of, but rather a moment to be excited about, since the positive emotions you've been stuffing deep down within you for years will now slowly come to the surface. The unconscious triggers that spur on bodily symptoms are now your conscious challenges. These challenges demand a new, intuitive response to them that takes a certain level of courage and emotion to implement consistently. The unforgiveness toward yourself and your past relationships that have weighed you down emotionally and physically for years will now have the potential to come out through your tears and dissatisfaction. The more often we allow this type of expression to come forth, the more willing we become to step out of our health anxiety identity. However, your inner child will flex its might in different ways, so be aware, especially as you allow your suppressed feelings to be expressed in targeted ways towards the people that need to hear it, including your own inner child for instance. If your own inner child needs to receive an update in terms of transitioning from old beliefs to new beliefs, make sure that it is a direct order and not a timid suggestion. A direct order is one that comes with a high level of emotional intensity and belief in what is real now, not what the inner child believes is real based on an experience you may have had when you were 5 years of age. That old blueprint of who we are and what the world is like is changing now, one day at a time.

Health anxiety is the start of a peaceful life, not the confirmation that this is in fact a way of life.

Your mental and physical symptoms must never define who you are and what you believe about yourself and the world. At this beginning stage of the healing process, you will come to realize how overly critical you have been of yourself and things that happened in your life. The energy you put forth into catastrophically labeling every little thing you feel in your body has drained your physical energy as well as your spirit-led life force faster than anything else. As the mind becomes overworked, so does the body. When the body feels overworked it will signal certain symptoms that portray the message of 'overwhelm'. This can lead to stuck energy in the head area that causes depersonalization and dizziness, two anxiety symptoms that go hand in hand and that affect a large majority of health anxiety sufferers.

We have made our lives complicated and dramatic out of an unconscious need to maintain our addiction to suffering. Struggle is what most of us have known for pretty much our entire lives, and the moment there isn't struggle we're suddenly unsure of how to handle the situation. Health anxiety presents just another symptom, one more way for us to struggle so that, unconsciously, we can continue to identify who we are within those struggles. It is a tiring process that keeps us occupied in thinking that we are living life the way we're meant to when, in fact, there is no written rule in the book of life that says suffering and struggle are necessary for true happiness. Looking at your own nervous habits from an outsider's perspective, it would make no sense that a simple idea could spur on a host of uncomfortable bodily feelings, but it does. Not because the idea is true or holds some sort of extreme power over us, but because we've never really considered that we had the strength to put our heart into forming new ideas altogether. A certain degree of courage is necessary for healing health anxiety because it takes courage to believe something that opposes your subconscious core beliefs and live it out daily with enough feeling for it to become your new core beliefs.

These core beliefs, the ones that surface as initial feelings in the body, are the captain that guides the ship toward its destination. If we look to eliminate or neglect the captain, the crew won't have any real destination to move toward and will eventually find itself lost at sea. Therefore, advice such as, 'don't think about it' or, 'just move on' creates opposing results to what we truly desire, because putting effort into not thinking about the threat created in the mind only makes us more nervous about what form of uncertainty will arise in our future. The human mind is not very good at 'not thinking about things', so how can we expect this strategy to work? It simply doesn't. A deeply sensitized health anxiety sufferer that is told to 'just move on' would like nothing more than to do just that, but due to the power of our 'reptile' brain coupled with our emotional brain (limbic system) we consistently seem to be brought back to fear. I'm not saying it's impossible to reach a point where you can just move on from what feels like a physical issue. No, what I am saying is that you may not yet be ready for such a big leap forward. You see, one moment of clarity or one epiphany is like one more small tick toward overcoming health anxiety and living through the perceptions of your higher self. Gather up enough ticks with a feeling of being capable of moving past this chapter of irrational fear, and you will be met with your new best friend, the unknown.

Once you meet with the unknown all sorts of new experiences start happening to you from an internal as well as external (situational) perspective. Your energy levels will increase, you will become more optimistic, and your life will slow down to a more natural pace. In turn, you will be aligning yourself with the flow of nature, and therefore manifest your desires more easily. It is imperative that you understand that the unknown is your friend, not your enemy. Not knowing what the outcome of an anxiety symptom will be is okay, not knowing what the outcome of a relationship will be is okay, and not knowing exactly how you will feel in uncertain moments is okay. It is all okay, this is the truth. Through this book, my goal is to help you de-value your need for control not only in reference to your health anxiety, but in life as well.

Control demands that we know the answer, trust allows the answer to come forth in time.

In later chapters, I will delve deeper into this new world of healing that we will all eventually encounter at some point. On these initial steps in our pursuit toward healing health anxiety, however, it is enough to simply come to grips with the idea that you've been living your life around a web of lies. These lies are due to a small handful of life experiences that the subconscious mind has stored as your personal reality. In this book I refer to the subconscious mind as your own inner child since it was during those early formative years that we unknowingly painted the picture of what reality means to us and defined our views of what we feel we are truly capable of. Little did we realize at the time that we were placing meaning on everything our five senses were picking up without consciously doing so. If we were told that we'd never amount to much as an adult, that became the blueprint of the life we would live, and as a result we unconsciously sabotage any good that defies this personal law. However, if we were repeatedly told that everything we touch turns to gold and that life would be fruitful for us we will unconsciously look to fulfill these laws instead. You may have been terrorized or neglected by an authority figure in your past which has created the blueprint you live with today. Sometimes it is one 'traumatic' event that paves the way for a deeply rooted belief (Initial Sensitizing Event), other times it comes down to repeated experiences (Subsequent Sensitizing Events). Recently, a client came to me wondering how he had come to suffer from health anxiety. As I helped him relax in mind and body, I asked him some very specific questions knowing that his own inner child was more open in those very moments to sharing its true beliefs. I asked him and his inner child which event had everything to do with this health anxiety pattern. The answer was felt, not thought, and appeared in the form of seeing his grandfather painfully pass away when he was young. As he shared this moment of clarity with me I immediately sensed that his fears around his health came from witnessing an authority figure go through moments of emotional and physical pain. He spent years looking to understand how he got to this state with little to no progress, and within minutes of embracing his inner child, he felt like he tapped into a big part of where his health anxiety manifested from, the initial sensitizing event. The understanding of his ISE wasn't going to be enough however; we needed emotional release, a full-on perceptual shift over his grandfather's passing, and to find the good in what was originally perceived as bad or traumatic. In this case, the bad was the pain and suffering that the grandfather had to go through, and my client had to be the witness of. This perspective through the process of emotional reframing turned into grandfather passing on wonderful life lessons, the gratitude of having optimal health now, and the privilege that grandfather in fact, lived a full and long life.

Time doesn't heal old wounds, time only makes the emotional suppression connected to them more evident through the body over time.

Never rely on logic or time alone to heal. You will only find yourself more frustrated and confused by life if you do so. Instead, understand that we're all on a spiritual journey whether we realize it or not, and healing health anxiety plays a major role in reaching enlightenment for each of us. You can think of enlightenment as clarity and flow. As no longer living by the rules set by others from the past combined with a sense of effortless contentment for life in the present. Through this experience of healing health anxiety, you have seized a great opportunity to defy the character you believe you need to play for society and will replace it with one that is simpler and unconditionally loving. No longer will you need to be a part of a race, a religion, a national party, a country, a culture etc.; these attachments will fade and all that will be left is to be truly human once again. Before health anxiety, there was making sense of the informational data coming in through your senses. During health anxiety, that past programming takes effect in the form of dread, pessimism, and fear. After health anxiety, our senses will no longer be threatened by the outside world but rather be accepting of all possibilities with trust, grace, and love.

At the initial stages of health anxiety, after a diagnosis of our mental and emotional health, we often look for the quickest path out of our suffering. However, if the subconscious blueprint we have of ourselves and our lives doesn't change there is no point in meeting with quick change anyway, since we will only sabotage it in some way as we fall back to old habits. The messy journey that comes in the form of new cognitive realizations, physical purging of the negative emotional weight, enacting new behaviors in the face of uncertainty, and imagining a new outcome for the future must all be embraced to become fully healed. As these experiences contribute to our new perceptual reality, we will begin tapping into a new sense of enjoyment, as what once threatened us starts to look different. I often hear people tell me how they had overcome health anxiety without even knowing they had done so. They were so focused on the process and on building positive momentum around the re-creation of their new identities that they never realized how their old, damaging ideas and bodily feelings no longer held the same amount of fearful weight on them. They became fleeting experiences for the healed, things that left as quickly as they showed up. This is the disinterest I set forth as being one of our vital goals on the path toward healing. Disinterest in irrational fear breeds inner peace, inner peace leads to a feeling of positive emptiness within, and positive emptiness paves the way for unconditional love, gratitude, and purpose. As you truly tap into it, it becomes a natural, step-by-step process. Throughout this book we will take each step together gently and self-lovingly.

Often when we take these unfamiliar steps forward, we also skip a few without knowing we've done so. This is okay, and is mainly due to the level of emotional intensity that accompanies the win we just had. For example, a health anxiety sufferer often feels their head pulsating and instead of going directly to the doctor for a check-up, (which of course should be done at some point) he or she just sits with it. Mentally, the person looks to understand the reasoning behind this bodily reaction and creates a new relationship with the symptom itself. Whether a clear answer arises or not doesn't matter, the old reaction turns into a conscious response which activates our intuition once again. As the symptom subsides over a short period of time, the experience and response to these types of spontaneous bodily symptoms lessen more and more, as the trust in our body's ability to heal without the need for the over-analytical mind rises. This is one such example of a win in my world, and they can show up in preparation for a challenging moment that may arise in the future, or spontaneously through instructions by the heart. Either way, a win is a win and at the end of the day, it's always best to count your wins consciously rather than allow your inner child to make you feel like the suffering has become too ingrained to reverse.

The inner child is creative and always looks for an opportunity to bring you back to your comfort zones.

A good example of this is when you haven't gotten the kind of quality sleep you need to maintain your progress over health anxiety. Your inner child clings to your vulnerability and presents a host of ideas and feelings to you that bring you back to a place of fearful comfort. This comfort zone is much more than just a place, it's a way of seeing the world and a way of seeing ourselves.

Seeing the light threatens the inner child because it is far too bright for it to comprehend.

A gentle and patient approach filled with reflections on our daily wins convinces the subconscious that it's okay to take further steps into a world that is unfamiliar. When the inner child brings up a defense mechanism which looks to pull you back into comfortable fear, you must notice it and respond to it in the same way you would for your own child. If you have children, you know how fulfilling it is to listen to your child's fears and concerns and directly guide them toward a new perspective altogether. Sometimes this is done solely through words, other times through sharing evidence or even new behaviors. When your inner child has a concern that is presented through an immediate thought, an immediate feeling in the body, or even through bringing your attention full circle to something in the outside world that it may feel threatened by, you must guide it down a new path. Don't run from this part of yourself, be your own guide instead. The inner child will feel listened to, understood, and acknowledged (something you may have never felt while you were a child). The adult conscious mind and the child unconscious mind begin the process of congruence as a new bond is built between mind and body, and between core beliefs and conscious beliefs. When this kind of harmony is built on the inside, there's nothing on the outside that can spur on fear, anger, disappointment, or impatience for long anymore. This is because the solution isn't seeped in a need for control anymore (controlling what the body projects), but rather in the embracing of a lack of control. This new path leads a health anxiety sufferer to no longer endlessly grasp at information that provides a sense of certainty, since certainty now seems like something that we wanted but never needed. No longer do we need that authority figure to tell us that our health is fine, we assume that role ourselves instead. No longer do we need someone to hold our hand to comfort us during a challenging moment, we do that with our own inner child instead. And no longer do we frantically search for a solution here and now. We are distancing ourselves from replaying survival-based ideas at this point and moving toward living freely in a world of possibility, and the distinction between good and bad lessens to the point where it no longer exists. We will continue to understand this new inner dimension toward the end of this book, but at this beginning stage, it is important to plant the seed of possibility and flexibility now so that when you meet it you are ready to embrace the new feeling.

In this first chapter, I brought forth the idea that you are suffering from a deep level of sensitivity toward the thoughts and bodily feelings that you are consciously and unconsciously interpreting as a present or future physical threat. Along these lines a sense of mentally 'losing it' may be coupled with your sensitivity, bringing about a feeling of emotionally 'standing guard' toward inner and outer information that could lead to losing control altogether. Remember that you are more than health anxiety. You are more than the limits and fears your inner child places over your life, and this is the major life experience you must go through in order to gain the tools you need to eventually do something meaningful and touching for others. Think of the health anxiety healing journey as progressively equipping you with the weapons and armor needed to take on life's future challenges. If you can adopt this attitude at this early stage of this book, you're already well on your way to becoming a warrior.

Chapter 2:
The Inner Tug of War

After recognizing the health anxiety within us, we soon find ourselves in a battle between wanting to believe in our good physical health and the possibility of ill health on the horizon. In this step, we become almost completely occupied in the mind and lose touch with the outside world to a large extent. At some point, we will re-learn how to communicate with the outside world again, but at this stage in the step-by-step ladder system we call 'healing' we are still victims of thought replaying.

Thought replaying is connected to a pattern of similar ideas that keep us stuck in the familiar emotional state that amplifies our threat perceptions.

We would love to wholeheartedly believe in the idea that these anxiety symptoms are just fleeting and normal bodily sensations. However, because they feel so similar to what we think physical illnesses and ailments feel like, we associate ourselves with being ill. Imagine going the entire day, every day, with your state of mind being so overly preoccupied with these bodily sensations that the idea of letting them go and allowing them to 'just be' scares you back into obsession over them. We fear that if we do let go and believe in a new perspective over them that the worst may truly arise. We even justify our 'standing guard' over them since our physical test results have all come back negative so far and we feel that one of the reasons for this run of good physical luck is our obsession over the bodily sensations. This, of course, is another clever defense mechanism by the inner child keeping us within the familiar patterns we now know as an addiction to suffering. As mentioned earlier, one of the main ingredients to health anxiety freedom is heartfelt trust, and yes, it can certainly trickle from one aspect to another.

For example, when you eliminate all jealousy within your relationship and give your partner the space and respect they want and deserve, you are building trust in other areas of your life as well. Initially, trust can cause a feeling of vulnerability, and since we have associated vulnerability with something negative, we rarely allow ourselves to trust in new, unfamiliar experiences, or place ourselves into new unfamiliar experiences. However, vulnerability is a stepping stone to inner peace. Without it there can only be suffering, there can only be health anxiety. One of my greatest achievements as I healed from my own health anxiety was my ability to befriend vulnerability, welcome it, and move with it every chance I had. This doesn't mean fighting through an experience or exposing yourself to the point of re-traumatizing yourself. It means respecting the part of you that hasn't been in this experience for long enough for you to feel safe within it. We feel unhealthy, but we aren't unhealthy. Don't believe everything you feel. Question your feelings as much as you question your thoughts and soon your fears will turn perceptually safe. This back and forth seesaw between wanting to believe in our good health and falling victim to demoralizing ideas around our health can be attributed to a tired mind. A tired mind means a tired body, which equals a tired spirit. In energetic terms, fear is the lowest frequency a person can emanate into the world. What we emanate we call back toward ourselves so that as much as our will demands us to believe in our good health, our vibration is sending a different signal altogether. Quite often I am asked what the best thing to do is within these moments of inner instability and uncertainty, and my answer depends on the person asking. If the person is more in the mindset of 'hoping' for better outcomes, they would need to develop the proper 'response' skill sets in moments of fear and doubt. However, if the person feels they have consistently attempted to respond within these moments differently and act in accordance with their desires, they may need to apply the art of 'inaction' instead. You have two options when it comes to your response to uncertainty connected to your health anxiety: you can either do something or you can do nothing.

Keep in mind that even doing nothing is doing something.

We have the ability to mentally replace old perceptions and ideas, speak up, enact a new behavior that defies the fear, or even imagine a greater outcome. We can even do none of these things and still send a clear message to the subconscious within our bodies that the threat perception it believes is justified is, in fact, false. Much like an experienced meditator who sits in peace listening to his or her breathing while simultaneously experiencing heart palpitations. They do not add logs to the fire and, by not adding more logs, the fire calms eventually, just as the mind and body can.

Many health anxiety sufferers often have the mistaken belief that they are lacking more vital information that will lead to the epiphany that will take them toward healing in a single moment. This sort of approach to healing only brings up more frustration because you are pushing for a solution that isn't there. The more you push, the less wisdom you will acquire, and wisdom is both the voice of your heart and the opposite of the voice of your mind. To understand whether you need to acquire mental, physiological, behavioral, or imaginative skill sets, or apply inaction, you simply have to be honest with yourself and look at your results. Have you been looking to fight your own inner demons without a spear? Do you feel helpless in moments of mental conflict between optimal physical health and potential ill health? If so, you need to acquire and prepare skill sets for the day ahead and apply them when you sense the fear arising again. Do you find yourself trying everything under the sun and getting no positive results? In this case, you need to take a step back and do nothing. Trust the part of you that allows for the mental or physical symptoms to be present without a need to do something about them. This isn't natural, of course. Inaction is a great challenge and a separate kind of skill set that goes against the messages within society today. We are told to be better, do better, speak better, act better, etc., but where does all this being better truly take us? It takes us toward a place where we are never content, rarely present, and often frustrated, that's where. Goals are good, obsession is bad. Nature's lessons are seeped with a balance that must translate into our own inner worlds. For example, I used to be the forcing type (I refer to this pattern as doer-ship). I forcefully applied Cognitive Behavioral Therapy practices, Neuro-Linguistic Programming, Emotional Freedom Techniques, and positive thinking. I even thought of stopping practices until I realized that I was only fueling the fire of my health anxiety further. When I realized this, I stopped and I took a few steps back. I practiced becoming an observer rather than a reactor. I 'allowed' rather than looked to change things, and I began building a new relationship with my body through my mind. It worked wonders.

To be free from health anxiety you must trust in the healing potential of your own body, and to trust in this healing potential you must get the over-thinking mind out of the way.

Thinking is good, overthinking is bad. Bad in the sense that it keeps our energies occupied in thinking that we're doing something right when in fact we're just chasing our own tails and running in circles. Oftentimes, when this is the case, health anxiety sufferers feel better by the evening because they're so exhausted from all the overthinking and inner fighting that they have no more energy left to give. They hold up a white flag to their sensations and intrusive thoughts and within it experience a glimmer of the present moment. It is scientifically proven, now, that a thought coupled with true heartfelt belief has the potential to affect the body (positively and negatively). In turn, the person responsible for your own suffering is you and no one else. No matter what you went through in the past, you are always one powerful new perception away from change. Taking responsibility at this stage in your healing is essential. Don't blame anyone, absolutely no one, not even God, for your current health anxiety life chapter. Blame burns up energy that could be used for better purposes. Every ounce of your focus and energy must turn to creating small 'wins' throughout the day, and these wins must feel like wins. A new association toward a bodily sensation, giving less authority to a friend or family member, more authority toward what you think, using more empowering words rather than staying stuck in victimhood, implementing the power of inaction, running an internal movie of how you want your day to go instead; these are all examples of health anxiety wins. Let me remind you, however, that more often than not we don't go searching for the opportunities to create these wins. Rather, the opportunities come to us, and intuitively we take them to move one step closer to safety perceptions within the subconscious mind.

Remember how we said that when you build trust in one aspect of your life it begins trickling down toward other aspects? The same goes for the other characteristics of you that you've unconsciously neglected as well. Let's take courage, for example. That moment when you speak up at the dinner table during a family gathering and share your brilliantly creative ideas is a courageous moment. Your inner child doesn't like this act of defiance, but you know that it will contribute to courageously accepting new ideas around your health soon enough, so you go for it. And what about unconditional love? I bet that for a very long time you felt like you needed to prove yourself in some way to feel love and worthiness toward yourself. Well, what do you think would happen if in one powerful moment you gave yourself a 2-minute self-hug for absolutely no reason at all? I'll tell you what would happen: your life would begin changing because you would begin changing. Soon enough the pressure to do something perfectly or become someone perfect (the masks we feel we need to wear) would be replaced with the full appreciation and acceptance of whatever is taking place at this very moment. This will lead to no longer resorting back to quick fixes for health anxiety, and inaction would once again couple with trust and self-love to bring about a greater faith in mind, body, and spirit.

Let me tell you a short story about a family friend I used to call uncle ...

My uncle was obsessed with the number and age 77. He never gave us the reason why this number was so meaningful to him, but he would consistently remind us that he wouldn't live past the age of 77. In his 70s he could walk for miles, was mentally sharp, and had the curiosity of a young child. He epitomized health in every way and was my role model in how to approach life's greatest challenges for a long time. When he turned 77 he developed an aggressive form of cancer (which I can conclude was out of the blue) and just before his 78th birthday he passed away. I believe to this day that the subconscious blueprint for his emotional, physical, and spiritual health was the direct reason for his passing. Just like how a computer program doesn't get completely deleted even when you send it to the trash can. My uncle's subconscious program was never replaced with an updated one, and I believe this contributed to his passing at what seemed to me to be an early age for someone like him.

These types of stories are lessons for us to take and use in our own lives. They are not meant to frighten us in any way, because in order to heal we must first turn our fears into something else; we must update the old software that's running in our own subconscious minds and replace it with a new one. To do this we must be open to what we are closed off from: our intuition. When speaking of intuition, we are recognizing our ability to make successful decisions without deliberate analytical thought. The mechanisms of intuition can be strengthened over time but only to the degree that we 'devalue' the answers that come from the analytical mind more and more as we go.

When there is a balance between intuition, intelligence, and instincts, we find our inner peace. We sense this balance within us where we can begin manifesting what we want with ease, even physical healing if we so choose. There are many health anxiety sufferers out in the world that believe that just because they think an idea around ill health about themselves that they will manifest it. I don't believe this to be the case since an idea is solely that, just an idea, unless coupled with other internal components to bring about a result. Ideas are meaningless if the inner child doesn't completely believe in the idea, and the inner child manifests its beliefs through feelings. Yes, we may be at a crossroads in terms of what to believe about our physical health now, but these ideas are similar to clouds floating in the sky. The most important choice we can make is whether we add feeling to an idea or not. At this juncture in your health anxiety healing, you mustn't get too caught up in whether the idea around ill health is true or whether it will manifest. Remember that the health anxiety healing journey is meant to reunite you with your non-judgemental and childlike sides again. That is what you're working toward. Your suffering and your healing are determined by how much emotion and belief you have in your ideas or feelings. Remember, an emotion is always coupled with a feeling, but a feeling is not always coupled with an emotion. A feeling is an initial unconscious perception about something and the emotion that follows is a confirmation of this perception based on what we choose to believe. If we choose to believe in our good physical health then we won't be caught up in a catastrophic idea or initial feeling, allowing it to die off and never be confirmed as a subconscious core belief.

You must choose who you want to be at any given moment of the day.

To be honest, I never knew that I had a choice of who I wanted to be as I went through my health anxiety days. I thought that if I thought it, felt it, or heard it (people's opinions of me) then that's who I was. This is what kept me stuck in the health anxiety loop. You see, your identity is formed through a bundle of characteristics that develop into patterns. These patterns we now know as being your 'persona parts'. For example, let's say that you've just become aware that you're going back and forth between thoughts of ill health and optimal health in your mind. In that very moment, you can activate the understanding parts of your persona and address your thoughts around ill health from a place of respect. Since the thought itself has no real basis of truth, you can see it as just another way the inner child within you is looking to keep you in a protective state. This state of being maintains our addiction to our stress hormones, which in turn confirms our core beliefs around our limits and justifies the idea that the world is a scary place to live in. Remember, your protective subconscious mind, your inner child, is a very opportunistic part of you that will do everything in its power to prevent any kind of mental, emotional, behavioral, and identity-based change. So, in that very moment, if you can bring your understanding and compassionate persona parts toward your fears of ill health, all of a sudden the inner child has no way to strengthen its fear perceptions and beliefs. You are literally cutting off its supply lines and moving to a place of being non-judgmental, no longer caught between the thoughts that you once deemed as good or bad. You are emotionally neutral, and it is in this very place where a conscious choice can be made in terms of what is really true and what is simply a survival based program. When you no longer engage with the very persona parts and reactions that spur on health anxiety you step away from being a sufferer and move toward the process of becoming a true healer yourself. To add to what was introduced earlier in the book, here are a few more examples of persona parts that get suppressed due to health anxiety:

The freedom to choose parts: This part reminds us that we have options on how to think, perceive, act, imagine, and be. In fact, almost all the health anxiety sufferers I've worked with through my online programs have told me that one of the biggest epiphanies that came to them while healing was the understanding that they must simultaneously reinvent themselves and get back in touch with their childlike parts once again. The only way to do this is to activate your freedom to choose a new meaning over something at any given moment of the day.

Your light-hearted parts: Life can be a dance, a joke. It doesn't have to be a serious one-way road to eternal suffering. These parts remind us that we can tap into the lighter side of things and take life less seriously, as children tend to do. How does this translate into health anxiety healing? Well, imagine for a moment that you listened to those scary voices in your head through the voice of a childhood cartoon character that you simply couldn't take seriously. What tends to happen then? Well, if you repeat this practice consistently the thought loses strength and becomes fleeting. It comes and it goes, and it never has the chance to affect us at a physiological level. These are the types of responses to fear that can change everything for the better. I recommend you immediately begin practicing listening to your catastrophic ideas through the voice tone of a funny cartoon character and write down your conclusions afterward. You will find that as you practice this you will begin seeing your worry and catastrophic ideas from a new point of view, one that sees through them rather than becoming them.

Your flexible parts: These parts have everything to do with perfectionism. When allowed to come out and play, you allow yourself to make mistakes and your mind and body become less rigid as a result. A stiffness in the mind affects the body and vice versa, but when we allow ourselves to say, do, and be what feels right, rather than what's been a subconscious program, we allow for the healing potentials within us to become activated once again. To view the world just as a young child would.

Remember, your intuition is always looking to connect and communicate with your conscious mind. When we allow our hearts to do so, we can begin opening to even more of these types of persona parts that we've suppressed due to fear for far too long. However, remember that you are going to have to sacrifice and let go of the way you default to your 'replaying' mind in order to solve all your inner and outer challenges. As you allow for your intuition to guide you, the ideas that once used to occupy your focus, energy, and behaviors will no longer be trustworthy. This journey will remind you that you're really just re-learning how to live your life freely rather than acquiring new teachings and applying them. You will have the sense that you're consistently going backward in order to go forward again. You will go backward in thought and imagination to re-perceive your core beliefs, to forgive yourself and others at a heart level, and to rebuild your relationships with your inner child and others once again. You will also find yourself learning from your childhood before you were corrupted by other people's beliefs and actions. That childlike purity, where life is light-hearted again, will arise as you continue to take advantage of the situations that cause an initial fearful feeling.

Moments of fear and anxiety hold within them the tremendous opportunity for re-programming.

When we can seize the opportunity within a moment of fear and work with it, we are taking back our true power from our subconscious mind that is determined to keep things the same and familiar, since its formula for life is to make familiarity equal to safety. This isn't a battle of beliefs so much as it is a directional shift that places the conscious beliefs and subconscious beliefs on the same page. This is where feeling and thought align, and where intuition and behavior are naturally one.

The beauty of this healing journey is that we no longer feel a need to always watch over our bodies.

This leaves plenty of time to be in the present, conserve energy, and truly live life the way it was meant to be lived. Health anxiety sufferers feel pulled toward watching over a body that can already heal itself better than any action the mind can take. The mental tug of war between trust and distrust in the body (and the changes of life) is tamed at this point. No longer do we feel the need to ask for a 5th, 6th, or 7th opinion regarding our health, and instead our primary support person within our relationships takes on a completely different role. This person may be your spouse, or your boyfriend or girlfriend, and instead of asking for reassurance regarding a sensation in your body, you begin asking what their day was like instead (for example). The focus is turned from you to us. This 'us' applies not just within your intimate relationships, but the 'us' that is this world. You will start feeling connected to everyone and everything at a deeper level, deeper than you ever have felt before, and this eliminates the reputation you've been working so hard to maintain (anxious) for the sake of others and your own inner child. You begin to no longer identify with being a sufferer when your trust in your body is built, and you begin identifying with infinite potentials.

For now, it's enough for you to tap into the idea that you are allowed to be whoever you want to be at any given moment of the day. This mindset will lead you to knowing what to do in moments of fear and health anxiety, allowing everything to stop becoming so mechanical in terms of skill sets. Knowing what to do in moments of sensitivity and fear is more important than thinking you know what to do. One is heart-led while the other is head-led; you may have a health anxiety spurring idea or a feeling that arises throughout your day, while simultaneously your heart sense is telling you to simply stay focused on the natural surroundings around you. You follow these orders and soon enough forget that you were almost pulled into health anxiety again. This is more so when moving toward truth rather than running from fear. You're not turning a blind eye to fear, but rather doing what needs to be done so that the old program loses its tight grip over you.

Like a butterfly ready to take its first flight, you go for it and allow life to teach you as you move forward.

Take a moment right now in the early stages of reading this important book and recognize what sort of knowledge you have deeply come into contact with that you can apply toward your healing right now. Sometimes it takes some deeper reflection, and other times it simply slaps you in the face, hard. As you recognize this new epiphany, spend time with it today and see where it leads you next. What other moments of clarity arise as you plant the seed of wanting to understand this original knowledge more deeply? You already have everything within you to heal your health anxiety, and I can say this because over the last decade I've helped thousands of people worldwide to heal their health anxiety for good. As we go forward to the next step on the ladder of health anxiety healing, let's acknowledge the courage within us to heal our emotional wounds once and for all. Let us also acknowledge the fact that we can find enjoyment in this winding, healing path that we are on. It's meant to be challenging for a specific reason, and soon enough you will truly understand what that reason really is.

Chapter 3:
The Inner Child vs The New You

Within this next phase of healing health anxiety, we will feel led toward fighting our inner and outer challenges at every turn. Competition, both internally and externally, overtakes cooperation and our stress response leads to our perceptions and behaviors during the day. If you sense that this is happening within you right now, it's okay. It's a phase, it's a chapter, it's just another step to learn from on this journey toward healing health anxiety. It's important to note that there will be times when your competitive persona parts need to come out, such as within your career, possibly. But also remember that you mustn't be the same person at work as you are in other areas of your life. This fighting spirit doesn't have to involve ideas and feelings that lead to health anxiety. In fact, the more you fight them, the stronger they will become. To fight our subconscious mind's belief system is to engage in a losing battle. Right now the simple understanding that fighting with yourself and others will only cause further strain is enough to move forward. Understand the power of coming to a new conclusion. With every new conclusion comes a new challenge around it, and with every new challenge accomplished comes a new conclusion. This circular cycle is what brings on the kind of momentum needed to heal the spirit even before healing health anxiety. More often than not, I see people move their focus from healing health anxiety to transforming themselves as a whole in a way that in turn heals health anxiety. This is when the whole process becomes something we get attached to. It is a good attachment; this attachment to the healing process makes everything around you look different, a good kind of different.

Let's look at an example of the fighting phase that many of us experience on this journey:

You're going through your day, calm and emotionally neutral, when all of a sudden a heart palpitation strikes out of the blue. You are stunned and afraid of what it may lead to, and unconsciously you get angry at yourself for experiencing this momentary feeling. You become hyper-focused on your heart, wondering whether it will happen again or not, and at the same time trying to maintain a sense of normality in the moment. The battle rages on between paying close attention to your heart out of fear, being led by thoughts of catastrophic potentials, and acting normal to get back to a sense of safety. The fight is between mind, body, and your present external experience. If this state of being is prolonged, the unconscious trigger that spurred on the bodily sensation will become justified and the belief itself will grow stronger. The franticness is happening on the inside for most and rarely shows up as behaviors in these types of moments out of fear of looking crazy to others. Like a bottle being filled up with liquid, it soon begins to overflow as the physical and energetic energy within becomes depleted. The more we question what may happen next, the faster we deplete ourselves to the point where many health anxiety sufferers experience a state of steady physical numbness due to a system that is too familiar with being overwhelmed. This numbness, which can also be interpreted as depersonalization, protects us from reaching the same levels of overwhelm and emotional intensity that we have in the past.

A non-sufferer that experiences a heart palpitation perceives it as a fleeting experience and soon moves their attention back to connecting with their present external reality. A health anxiety sufferer views this sort of response as having the potential of making things worse in the future. This creates a feeling of not caring for the self, which could potentially have catastrophic physical consequences for them. More often than not, this approach comes from an overbearing parent who associated over-worry with love and care. This is present in many cultures around the world.

We tend to interpret the meaning of love as being worried for ourselves and our own children unconsciously until we realize what it is that is really taking place and how much energy loss is happening. Once we recognize that we have adopted this connection between worry and love we must address it relentlessly in both thought and behavior. A good starting point is to begin by breaking it down piece by piece and recognizing what price you are really paying for maintaining this meaning around love, and what love really means to you consciously. Be warned, however, that you may feel like you are separating from the generational patterns ingrained in your family tree. You may initially feel like you would be less loving and caring for the person you adopted this pattern from. Resistance to change will always be present in one form or another by the inner child. It's up to you to understand the reasoning for this resistance and to work with it going forward. In my life, for example, I initially had the feeling that everything was falling apart around me when in reality it was all just starting to come together in its own beautiful way.

We go into fight mode in order to stay one step ahead of anything that could potentially go wrong.

This fight mode not only affects us internally, but we also start looking to control lives and situations of the people around us that we feel are out of our control as well. We quickly become obsessed with the need for certainty and begin to see uncertainty as the enemy, when in fact uncertainty itself has its own flavor, its own taste within life that must be respected and experienced as well. This doesn't mean that it's a straightforward approach to move from a mindset of fighting to one of observing or cooperating. If a person feels like their life is on the line, they will naturally and instinctively do everything in their power to find balance once again. Unfortunately, for a health anxiety sufferer, this feeling of having your life on the line has a constant presence. The feeling is at the forefront for most of the day, with only short snippets of distraction and calmness.

As we understand this more deeply, your default emotional state will look to survive for as long as possible, like tiny life forms looking to grasp onto whatever information keeps them alive. In this case, the default emotional state is fear and tends to be justified unconsciously first before consciously building on the original perception of threat. The body reacts, the mind accepts, and the spirit becomes fully invested in survival mode at every turn. In this state, the human electromagnetic frequency that radiates from the heart is sending the signal of extreme fear and doubt. As another person comes within 6 feet of a health anxiety sufferer the unconscious conversation between them is already in the process. If the other person is conscious of what the health anxiety sufferer is feeling at that moment of unconscious interaction, they will notice the walls being put up around them and the world. Conversations rarely have a sense of flow to them and are greatly shortened due to the opposing emotional states that are interacting with one another. To survive a conscious conversation with a non-sufferer is like being at war. The topic of conversation is rarely remembered, but how the health anxiety sufferer acted and what they said is certainly reflected upon in depth. As disappointment appears post conversation, the health anxiety sufferer is reminded of how challenging it is to be around others, let alone to speak up. A retreat toward the comforts of home, certain people, as well as worry becomes necessary at this point to them.

The thing about someone going through health anxiety is that they will spend an excessive amount of time reflecting on their experiences and often focus solely on what they did wrong or what went wrong.

This doesn't mean that the ideas they come across during their time analyzing the conversations are true. It simply means that the patterns of self-sabotage and inner suffering are alive and thriving inside them. Nothing is either true or false until we believe that it is. What may seem like a disastrous experience to you may have been a pleasant experience to another person. Healing is kind of like building Lego. When we defy our core beliefs, our instincts, and our inner child defense mechanisms that want to keep us in a familiar fearful space, we place more pieces on top of the new project we are working on building. When we succumb to our old mental and emotional patterns and aren't willing to sacrifice some of our habits for long-term change, those same Lego pieces get taken down one by one. Back and forth the fight goes on until a time when the person completely surrenders to everything that needs to be done to heal. However, as we commit to responding to life's challenges through our higher selves those same Lego pieces continue to build until the point of completion. When complete there is a sense of arrival as well as a sense of flow that gets integrated into everything we once saw as problems. When the project has been completed, we 'do' things differently and we understand more deeply what surrender means.

To surrender is not to give up on yourself; it is to give up on the habits that have perpetuated your suffering. Logically we understand the power of surrendering to uncertainty and moving gracefully toward the unknown. Doing it daily, however, is challenging, since healing is rarely a linear path. But just because something is challenging doesn't mean we should neglect it or look toward what comes easy to us. Once all your Lego pieces are in place and the project (your new identity) is built, it becomes next to impossible to demolish it. There is too much momentum at that point. The person knows in their heart that an idea given focus and emotion to will turn into a belief, and so they become very picky as to which ideas are given priority. They no longer believe what they initially feel, but rather they see the feeling as a temporary interpretation made by their subconscious mind or body. Even good feelings are to be questioned when a person has completed their Lego project in its entirety. If a good feeling is the result of an upcoming purchase, the reaction to a compliment made by another, or due to a win by their favorite sports team, they know that it is fleeting and will leave as quickly as it came. If the good feelings connected to these types of experiences are invested into deeply, the person will once again find themselves becoming an emotional yo-yo constantly at the mercy of the outside world to bring them a sense of joy.

The good feeling brought on by a sense of inner progress, a sense of empowerment, and the proudness brought on by the new habits now being a part of their lifestyle will last forever.

Optimal health and a clear and focused mind aren't something a health anxiety sufferer is used to, and so it will take them some time to get used to them. There will be times when this person feels like they are thinking and feeling nothing and may become frightened in the process. This reaction will only last as long as they decide it will last, since the moment they recognize that this is what inner peace actually is they will begin befriending the experience instead. Quite often people will come to me and tell me that they no longer suffer from health anxiety but feel a sense of depression coming on instead. I tell them what great news this really is! The irrational fear has receded and the opportunity to start anew has arisen.

Depression, within the healing of health anxiety, is a grey area. It is the next step on the ladder, and though it is not easy, it is still progress. This grey area demands that we place new meanings on things internal and external. For example, when you look in the mirror what do you see now compared to before? When a dog is barking outside does it mean you are compassionate toward it or aggravated by it? When an anxiety symptom arises, do you work to guide it or react in accordance with its perceptions of the world? When you're about to go to sleep and you can hear your neighbors laughing outside, do you get upset or see it as a sign of positive energy?

Do not use depression as another way to meet with the familiar state of victimhood.

You must see depression not as a step back, but as a stepping stone toward creating new associations between things. For example, the first time I felt depression during my health anxiety healing journey I lacked the motivation to do anything and just waited for it to pass. The fear cycle came back along with another bout of depression that was different from the first time. The second time around I took advantage of this new state of being and began to reorganize my thoughts, beliefs, and actions. I was gentle toward myself. I gave my mind, body, and spirit just what it was asking for: guidance. Like a pet owner teaching their pet rights from wrongs, I took the reins and slowly but surely brought neutrality and pleasant perceptions back into my life. The meanings that other people place on feelings and experiences don't have to be yours, even if the meaning comes from a place of authority. People are sure of nothing, even if they speak and act like they are. It comes down to a sense of self-worth. Maintaining the identity they were told they were when they were a child becomes a lifelong struggle to maintain. So much of our suffering comes down to this; to maintaining our reputations and therefore our identities. Many, however, realize along this journey that only when their reputation is torn apart can they then start fresh. We must separate ourselves from this rollercoaster. We must be brave enough to make mistakes, say or do the 'wrong things', and to let go when our hearts tell us to. When we come to realize that the need for control has been our biggest enemy for all these years, we can begin to lose control. Losing control doesn't mean giving up on a life experience you're meant to live fully. It simply means to ride the waves of what comes your way. We have control over less than a handful of our internal mechanisms, and it is necessary that we work with these, as they are the very things that will bring peace back to our life experiences. Remember, any change you make in any aspect of your life will trickle down toward your healing from health anxiety as well. As mentioned earlier, trusting a friend will soon lead to trusting in your optimal health in moments when you are experiencing bodily symptoms. Finding the courage to tell your father how terrorizing he really was when you were a child will transfer into the courage to stand up against your own inner child who looks to pull you back into the addiction to suffering.

Everything is connected, and everything you do or don't do matters in the big picture. It's important that you give yourself the credit you deserve right here and right now. By simply reading this book from cover to cover you are equipping yourself with the knowledge, skill sets, and lessons that will lead to a whole new world for you. Let's put health anxiety aside for a moment. You're heading in the direction of meeting your true purpose in this lifetime. Your true purpose doesn't necessarily have to be connected to the income you bring in or the career you choose. It may be the book you always wanted to write, the people you always wanted to help, or simply building back your relationship with mother earth and nature once again.

You deserve the very best and to get there you must first grow out of anxiety as a whole once and for all.

Think about the last bit of that sentence for a moment: growing out of anxiety. For so long something we felt was a necessary addition to who we were as a person now holds no value within it, since it's the value we place on anxiety that maintains its power over our perceptions and feelings. When you start arguing with your boyfriend or girlfriend and these arguments become routine, you start to question your relationship and the relationship loses its value to you and possibly the other person. Just like the experience between your adult, experienced, logical, conscious mind and your subconscious mind, which is basically the storage bank for all your life experiences. You no longer agree with its way of seeing things, so you slowly start distancing yourself from anything that reminds you of its ideas. When this occurs, it is less of a separation and more of a collaboration since we cannot rid ourselves of all that is the subconscious mind, but only share with it our new truths about our identity and life. If the subconscious mind weighs threat versus safety by our emotional reactions to each experience, then the less emotionally engaged we are in any given moment the less interest it will show, and the less need there will be for anxiety.

This brings up a very important part of the subconscious mind that connects to your health anxiety, known as the reticular activating system. This is your brain's filter system that filters out information that is unimportant to you. There are way too many things for your mind to cope with at once, so out of all the information you are bombarded with from moment to moment you turn your focus toward the information that is of value to you. When something you once feared no longer has the same emotional reaction to it, its value is lessened leading to no longer having to focus on it. Your five senses literally begin to reorganize what it gives priority and attention to based on the meaning and value you've consciously placed on things. The reticular activating system also becomes activated around information that poses a threat to you. For a health anxiety sufferer who is at the height of their physical fears, most things pose a threat anyway. Therefore, setting goals works very well while healing. But remember, when it comes to setting goals, make sure you set them in terms of what you want and not what you want to be rid of. To be specific is also very important for this process. A goal like 'I don't want to have health anxiety anymore' is too vague and involves the word don't. As the subconscious mind doesn't do very well with negations, it will skip words like not, won't, don't, cannot, and never, and moves to the next word in the sentence. So, to the subconscious mind this goal translates into 'I want to have health anxiety'. A better way of putting it would be 'I now allow myself to bring about new perceptions and inner peace to anything that resembles anxiety'. As you can see, this goal plants the seed of intention. The intention is to cooperate with a system within us that solely wants to protect us out of unconditional love. The anxiety is simply an overreach of the powers that this system has. By simply adopting this mindset of working with the feelings, thoughts, and habits that spur on anxiety you are 50% ahead of anyone else out there looking to heal, because the fighting has stopped. When the fighting and striving to fix something stops, an energetic reversal starts to occur.

The internal grappling you've been doing in your mind between threat perceptions and safety, negativity, and positivity comes to a halt and we can fully accept that this is our reality for the moment, but not forever.

Our core beliefs were formed through observation and experience, and they can change. Now when we observe, we observe through the eyes of someone who is no longer 'caught up' in a cycle of fear. When we have an experience, we are no longer having the experience through the lens of our survival brains. We are having an experience through the mind, body, and spirit of someone who is looking to start fresh once again. Therefore, the experience feels different—different is what we once feared but now accept as a part of the healing process. Core beliefs are so powerful that they have the potential to prevent us from seeing what's right in front of us. Health anxiety sufferers miss opportunities all the time because this is the case for them.

A new wonderful relationship gets sabotaged because of the core belief that says we are not worthy of being in a relationship. Therefore the bodily symptom arises as a protective measure in order to get the person out of that interaction, and as a result, out of the relationship as well.

A creative endeavor that would open us up to a new career for us gets pushed aside because of a core belief that says I simply don't have the skills to follow through. The core belief shows up as an initial feeling that is accompanied by bodily symptoms in order to meet the goal that the subconscious mind has for the person, which is to escape back to what it deems as being safe.

The power to heal lies within our awareness of that exact moment when a core belief wants to lead our decision making process. When you act out of conscious awareness, your higher self can act as a guardian for your mind. You are no longer led by your core beliefs, but instead you are now updating them and installing new ones. This can be a new act of the mind, an act of behavior, an act of words, or an act of the imagination. Any one of these four responses to a fear reaction, when coupled with a sense of certainty, will lead to a win for inner peace and eventually establish a new core belief and initial feelings. Let me give you an example of each so that you can implement them at any moment your health anxiety arises in the future:

Thought:

Core belief: Could this bodily sensation be the start of a physical illness?

Conscious belief: This bodily sensation is a protective response to a perceived fear.

Behavior:

Core belief: I must avoid all contact with other people at this party just in case my anxiety kicks in.

Conscious belief: I will gently and slowly interact with others as I show my body that both the people and this environment are safe.

Words:

Core belief: Don't say a word, you may spur on anxiety symptoms if others don't understand where you're coming from.

Conscious belief: Suppression is suffering, expression is healing, therefore I will speak my mind for the sake of showing my own inner child that I have important and worthy ideas to share with the world.

Imagination:

Core belief: As I wake up in the morning, I imagine my day being a battle between suppressing the anxiety in my mind and my bodily symptoms.

Conscious belief: As I wake up, I imagine my day cooperatively moving forward with any anxiety that wants to show up throughout the day.

At this early stage of the book, I want to make it clear to you what format I believe works best to gather positive momentum in the face of health anxiety. It's important that you take note of this structure and

begin introducing yourself to the components mentioned right away:

Morning: Internal movies

If someone asked me what the most important tool was that contributed most to my health anxiety healing, I would say my imagination. Little do we realize that every feeling or idea that gets coupled with emotional intensity creates a picture or movie in our minds. This way of unconsciously imagining creates a slideshow for future experiences, and we are literally writing up the stories for our day without even realizing it.

Upon waking up, run the internal movies of exactly how you want your day to go. You don't have to be good at conscious visualization since your subconscious mind will already pay attention to your intent. You will get better the more you practice this. For now, just imagine in full vivid color with all your senses engaged on how you want your day to go, from getting up in the morning all the way until your head hits the pillow at night. Take your time, don't rush, and even be courageous enough to step into the internal movie you are running. Go a step further and play with your mental movies. Playfulness is a vital component in healing whereas seriousness cuts us off from deeper inner development. Eliminate the need to run the internal movie perfectly, just run it.

Einstein once said, "Logic will get you from A to B. Imagination will take you everywhere."

Throughout the day: Thought reversal

As you go through your day, focus on reversing any thought that normally causes health anxiety, or any anxiety for that matter. Naturally, you cannot reverse every thought, but you can take note of which thoughts play out most often. An example of a thought reversal would be:

Rather than thinking, 'I'll never overcome health anxiety', think to yourself 'I'm in the process of healing health anxiety and enjoying the journey' instead.

Or

'I hope that same anxiety symptom doesn't show up today' to 'If that anxiety symptom arises today I will make sure to see it for what it really is, an anxiety symptom and nothing more'.

Keep in mind that your diet and sleep patterns play an important role in how effective your internal movies and thought reversals are throughout the day. Sometimes it's not the skill set or ability that prevents us from implementing a skill, but a lack of a meal.

Throughout the day: Words and behaviors

I've grouped these two together because they are more noticeable interactions with the outside world. In terms of words, let's focus on eliminating any words toward others that clearly indicate that we are stuck in a health anxiety loop. Many times, these words are connected to a need to receive something from someone else, known as secondary gains. It's important to admit your own secondary gains if they are present in your words. Aside from secondary gains, your words must come with a sense of making progress. This doesn't mean positive speaking; it means truthful speaking. Speak to others about your progress, about the changes you are encountering, and how you're gaining a sense of enjoyment during the healing journey. Remember, what others think about what you say is out of your hands and doesn't matter one bit. What's most important right now for you is adding more Lego blocks to the creation of your new identity, and your words are vitally important for moving toward this goal.

When it comes to behaviors, it's important that you step out of your comfort zone and expose yourself to your fears and doubts, but be careful you don't overwhelm yourself. If you step too far outside your comfort zone there is the potential to fall back into your comfort zones and re-traumatize yourself. However, if you are led by your intuitive heart sense and implement your exposure work in a safe and slow manner you are sure to benefit. A new behavior could simply be taking a new driving path home after work. Although this may take a few extra minutes away from getting to your destination, it will give you the sense of 'different' and uncertainty, which is what we want to befriend. Or, you may want to use more hand gestures throughout your day to show others how passionate and certain you are about what you're speaking about. Good. Remember, everything you do that feels new isn't something separate from who you really are. These new things are just parts of you that you've unconsciously chosen to suppress over the years.

Since change will be a necessary component to healing health anxiety, I personally thought it was a great idea to introduce change to my inner child in different ways. I began brushing my teeth with my opposite hand, walking backward in my living room, and even repainted every wall in my house to change my environment. The first time I walked backward in my living room my inner child told me that I would hurt myself and that I was wasting my time being foolish. The second time I did it I remember memorizing the walking path, which made my inner child feel safer walking backward, and I already felt less foolish. The third time and every subsequent time after, it began to bring with it a sense of wonder and fun. BINGO! I had altered an initial perception of my inner child. Too many people give up too soon when it comes to their change work because the inner child tries to deceive you with ideas that sway your focus. By giving up too soon they find themselves starting over again and again. Don't let this be you.

Starting today you get to choose who you want to be by imagining what is in line with your inner goals, thinking and perceiving in ways that bring emotional neutrality, speaking your truth, and having a sense of finally freely living out the childhood that you weren't allowed to live.

Chapter 4:
The Endless Search for
Health Anxiety Support

I'd like to talk simply in this chapter as someone who knows what it's like to suffer as well as heal from health anxiety. This step in the health anxiety healing journey can be one of the most confusing (and frustrating) in a person's lifetime. I'm talking about the windy path toward finding the proper support for healing, along with the skill sets and supplements that will actually work for you. I do believe that there is a place for anti-anxiety and antidepressant medications on the road to recovery, so let's not shun these pathways altogether, since there is much learning that can be done through them and some people are certainly in dire need of such options, if just temporarily.

It's my hope that with the understanding and implementation of what is within the pages of this book you will have a clearer understanding as to how to support yourself better, along with how to look for support from the outside.

Understand this point right now: the best health anxiety support you will ever find is within your own conscious mind.

This point must be understood as we recognize that any external support system we feel will support our journey is only an added bonus and not a necessity. What is a necessity is learning how to communicate with your subconscious mind through conscious acts and having the courage to live out the changes you make in the mind. Your conscious mind can also be viewed as your thinking brain. Structurally, this is your Neo Cortex. This thinking brain is what sets humans apart from all other species. To unleash the thinking brain into our everyday life we must first understand the types of resistance it faces on a daily basis that make us revert back to preprogrammed, unconscious ways of seeing things and acting:

1) **We instinctively resist anything that conflicts with how we see ourselves.**

    If we have an identity that has been so well established (anxious, worrying, undeserving, unlovable, sufferer, etc.) that it has become the blueprint for how we see ourselves as a whole, and we decide to change aspects to it as adults, resistance will inevitably show up. This is when the person must understand the intentions of their own inner child rather than fall for excuses as to why change is difficult and mustn't be attempted. Remember, we are rebuilding a relationship with our bodies, which you now know as being an extension of your own subconscious mind. Just like with any new relationship, the beginning is always unsteady and brings with it a feeling of vulnerability. Embrace it and make sure you don't shy away from it.

2) **We instinctively resist anything that comes into conflict with how we think others will see us.**

Whether we've been the anxious type around others for a while or have hidden our anxieties from others up to this point consciously or unconsciously, we'll instinctively look to maintain this way of presenting ourselves to the world. The thinking brain faces a great challenge here to perceive things differently. However, like all things in the world that change, we must deeply understand that we must change as well. With change can come great sacrifice and you must be willing to sacrifice your identity and reputation for the sake of something so much better.

3) **We instinctively resist anything that conflicts with what we see or believe to be true.**

Remember, you have core beliefs and conscious beliefs. Your core beliefs are your more deeply held beliefs, which show up as feelings toward things and experiences. Your conscious beliefs are the things you want to believe in, but consistently get overrun by your core beliefs. For example, a person can use positive affirmations toward their own health until they're blue in the face (conscious beliefs) but feel something completely different (core beliefs) which shows that there is a lack of congruence here. We must, at a core level, believe that we are worthy and capable of optimal mental, emotional, physical, and spiritual health, as well as consciously bring it with us from moment to moment for congruence to arise. This connection between feeling and desire is what creates our reality, and for a health anxiety sufferer it is what will allow them to move forward and away from identifying with being a sufferer.

The thinking brain is not your overthinking brain.

When we live in a state full of vibrant energy, health, and inner peace, we are allowing our hearts (intuition) to make the majority of the decisions for us throughout the day. However, at times the situation doesn't align with who we are molding ourselves into, so the thinking brain must intervene and show our instincts what's true for us now at this juncture in our lives. The taking of responsibility for the health anxiety chapter we are facing in our lives right now is a big task for most individuals. Looking inwards rather than outwards for support and answers is new, challenging, and even rewarding. We start to build trust in ourselves that we can guide our bodies toward perceptions of safety rather than succumb to its catastrophic interpretations of present or upcoming situations based on information gathered from our past. Yes, it certainly helps to talk to someone, to have them beside us in our moments of escalating fear, but these instances mustn't become habit. For if they do, we will only find ourselves slaves to the comforts and words of others. We are capable of healing health anxiety ourselves; this is an idea that must turn into a belief. In order to do so, we must use one of our most powerful tools for healing for our own benefit: our internal dialogue with the body.

A two-way conversation.

When the body speaks (bodily symptoms), the thinking brain must respond and take action following this mental guidance. The conscious mind must always be ready to share safety messages to the body at any given moment. In order to do so, however, we must slow down and become compassionately present with our bodies in that very moment. Just as a mother holds their newborn in their arms gently, slowly, and presently, so must the conscious mind be just as present with the body during the moments it speaks out (bodily symptoms). This response doesn't mean the symptom will automatically subside; the result is outside our control. However, how we respond to the symptom is within our control. Many people I know who have healed themselves fully admit that they had to turn their focus from the result to the process, from the future back to the present. Just as a newborn may take time before their crying stops, so may the body take time before the symptoms subside. Therefore, reinvesting your energy in a new direction is vitally important, since this energy that comes with what you focus on is finite, not infinite. If you give your energy away to petty things such as gossip and drama you will never be able to conjure up the energy needed for your conscious mind to communicate directly with your body in the moments when you need it to. Unless you can preserve this energy, your reaction to your symptoms will continue to be of a frustrated and fearful nature rather than of a nurturing and understanding nature.

The conscious mind has 3 primary functions:

1) Association: What you perceive through your senses you associate with past experiences; these can be overwritten as time goes on.
2) Perception: The act of interpreting your reality through your 5 senses.
3) Evaluation: After you have perceived, you evaluate. You do this by referencing your conscious mind's associations.

The conscious mind is your greatest support system, it really is. It gives us the ability to 'frame' (how an issue is posed or presented) the past, present, and future differently. But just like any other tool, it takes time to master it. To master your mind is to master your feelings and your body. Internally dialoguing with the body is quite foreign to many health anxiety sufferers but it does present a new way of communicating with the bodily symptoms that create such fearful reactions. Within your inner dialogues, you can use words like 'slow' to remind the body that the threat it has picked up is only perceived and not real. Or, the word 'trust' to remind the body that the present environment is safe and can be trusted. Your intuition will certainly guide you toward how to converse with your bodily symptoms in order to bring about a sense of safety and protectedness. But mastering your inner dialogue is just one way to begin the process of turning your core beliefs around. We must consider the real password to your subconscious mind, which is visual imagery, which you will hear me talk about often in this book because of its enormous ability to tame irrational fear for good.

The language of the 'reptile brain' is visual imagery.

All modern mammals have this reptilian complex, including humans, that is considered the driving force behind health anxiety. Among the traits generated through the reptile brain is the drive to establish and defend territory. Information that enters the brain must first go through the filter of the reptile brain so it can organize the data properly. If the environment and everything within it is deemed safe, the mammalian brain (responsible for emotions) connects a certain emotional attachment to the experience (in this case a neutral emotion).

All sensory data enters the brain stem (reptile brain) first before it proceeds toward the mammalian brain (emotional brain) while the neocortex is the last to be informed.

If the reptile brain is the seat of our instincts, the mammalian brain is the seat of our feelings and emotions. Both get activated based on experiences. If the reptilian brain is to be tamed enough to turn old threatening perceptions into safety, therefore altering the memories connected to our past traumas, we must use pictures and movies to re-wire these perceptions. Imagery has become the staple of my work in the last decade of helping people going through health anxiety, and so in this chapter, I introduce you to one of my most powerful imagery-based remedies that you can use on a daily basis.

Welcome to image cycling.

Originally created by Bill Bengston, image cycling speaks directly to the reptile and emotional brains and has the potential to heal everything from stuck emotions to physical illness (as was the case in my own mother's healing from ovarian cancer). Image cycling is simply cycling through a group of images back-to-back over and over while speeding up the process as time goes on. The process I outline below is not exactly the same way it was originally presented to the public, but I've found this method works to bring about the feelings needed to manifest these images into reality.

Step 1: Write down 5 areas of your life where health anxiety is negatively affecting you. This could be at work, in a relationship with someone, in the morning upon waking up, in the evening prior to going to bed, or anytime in the day where health anxiety is negatively affecting that particular experience.

Step 2: Underneath each of these 5 areas, write down exactly how you would prefer for that experience to go instead. At work, would you rather be outgoing and friendly? Write that down. Upon waking up in the morning would you rather be calmly doing a stretching routine? Write that down. This is where you begin planting the seed through your own consciousness as you move away from imagining the worst each and every day to consciously imagining the best.

Step 3: Close your eyes and create a picture of what you want. Base this around what you wrote down in step 2. Create your own image of that exact result and imagine it in your mind's eye. Do this for all 5 areas of your life so that you have 5 pictures ready in your mind.

Step 4: With your eyes closed, imagine each picture one by one in detail. Use color, sound, smell, and anything else that makes that outcome feel real and allows you to attach more feeling to it. You may even be screaming the word 'YES' in one of your pictures to emphasize your gratitude for healing health anxiety in that very aspect of your life.

Step 5: Rotate between your imagined pictures, moving on to the next image every 10 seconds. Once you've done this a few times, reduce the time between pictures to 5 seconds, then again to 2 seconds, and continue until there is less than a second between each picture you are cycling through. You may ask your spouse or friend to use a gong or singing bowl to remind you to proceed to the next picture and speed up over time, or you may also use an app that would help the process. Eventually, it's best that you find your own rhythm and do this on your own. The whole process can take as long as you'd like, but the key is to believe that it's already happened. I usually do it right upon waking up in the morning for a 2 - 5 minute period followed by leaving it alone, not reflecting on it or expecting anything to arise. Remember, focus on how you are proceeding with these skill sets, and how much feeling and certainty you are attaching to the exercises rather than worrying over when the result may show up. This is how inner trust is built on this journey.

I have created an introduction to Image Cycling on my YouTube channel. To find it, type in 'Image Cycling The Anxiety Guy' into the search bar and it will show up. Note that this is an intro video that is different to the advanced technique I have just presented to you. So eventually I would prefer you to use the process I just mentioned daily for at least a few weeks.

The reptile brain will begin altering its immediate associations in any given environment, paving the way for the conscious mind to think rationally while the inner child (subconscious mind) will begin altering its interpretation of past traumas and experiences through image cycling and similar imagery-based work.

These types of skill sets create a sense of empowerment within ourselves, which allows us to be less reliant on other people and things for our healing. Healing health anxiety can be lonely at times, and it's meant to be that way. The lessons you take from each step on the healing ladder cannot be learned anywhere else, and should be treated as a spiritual endeavor more than anything. When I use the word 'spiritual' I'm not talking about fluffy, poofy concepts, but rather an internal mindfulness journey to a place of greater clarity as to how life should be lived, and separating what is no longer important to us from what is. Your emotional maturity is very much a spiritual growth no matter what kind of beliefs you grew up with, and it's time to embrace it. I now have gotten to the point where the only company I need is myself, and I love spending time with me. I no longer feel alone but rather feel connected by spending time by myself. At one time I would be deemed a 'loner' living my life this way, but I've come to believe that it's meant to be this way in order for the true epiphanies to show up.

Disconnection and reconnection are very much a part of the health anxiety healing process. Disconnection from things that don't fulfill the soul long-term and the reconnection with things that do. Artificial stimulation like TV, gossip, video games, and social media no longer have the same value to us. We are now being led toward natural stimulations such as nature, physical contact, grounding, and dancing. You will, of course, have moments of giving in to the temptations of artificial stimulation and this doesn't mean you are in the midst of a setback. It just means that you haven't attached enough pain to your old connections and habits. When we connect more pain to something, we become more and more disconnected from it. On an opposing front, connecting pleasure to new habits will drive us in their direction.

Pain and pleasure are the two greatest motivational factors you need. If you are having trouble detaching from gossip which, for example, is only spurring on the stress hormones that are re-connecting you to health anxiety, you must find more reasons for why gossiping is unhelpful for you long term. Some reasons could be that it uses up too much of your vital life force, your energy. Or perhaps it takes up too much of your focus which distracts from where your focus and energy should really turn to, like toward the inner dialogues between mind and body. In the long term if you keep this habit up, what will you miss out on? Will it affect your physical health? Are you okay with this? Pain, Pain, Pain!

On the opposing side, how will distancing yourself from gossip help you eliminate your health anxiety?

Here is where the pleasure aspect comes in. You can certainly make better use of your time, not feel as drained afterward, and engage in more creative activities that you have always wanted to pursue. If I've realized one important lesson in my own health anxiety journey, it is that we don't have to be so afraid of change. We can welcome change with loving arms. I'm a big believer that many health anxiety sufferers are uncomfortable with being completely healthy since it has never really been a part of their lives before. Suffering, in some way, has been the blueprint for their lives, and each time things feel good they interpret it as a form of emptiness, they fear it, or fear it will be taken away from them quickly. This is most likely sitting at an unconscious level for most, and once it is brought to our awareness it can begin unraveling.

Be open to learning from unexpected sources.

As I mentioned earlier, this is a step-by-step process similar to that of climbing a ladder. Each rung on the ladder brings you closer to your destination, but it can also induce some level of fear or pleasure depending on your perceptions. If it is your first time climbing such a ladder, each step may induce more fear, and if you have been there before it may include more curiosity and excitement. In terms of health anxiety support, the most unlikely of supporters will cross your path, and I'm not talking about people, per se. For example, during a certain chapter in my healing I came across a unique looking tree on a natural pathway I was walking through back home in Vancouver, BC. I had the sense that I should sit with this tree, and so I did, right across it on a bench. The tree swayed with every gust of wind, but it never fell. The leaves on the tree fell, but never rotted, even in their new environment on the ground. There was a comforting energetic communication between me and this tree letting me know that there is nothing to fear, not even death.

The most unlikely sources can be the source of much of your healing if you can enter into each day of your life with curiosity and an open heart.

A rock, a bus, a river, a local shop; anything can be a guide to tapping into the answers you seek within yourself. You may be thinking 'this seems a little far fetched for me right now, Dennis,' and to that, I say 'I understand'. Each step on the healing path demands new feelings, new perceptions, and new lessons to be taken to heart. If you are not comfortable with something in this book or elsewhere, that doesn't mean that it is bad or that you should set it aside. Before, you may have deemed it as being wrong because of its unfamiliar nature, but I'm hoping you no longer see things as good or bad, but rather simply as experiences. Our life experience comes down to the way we perceive our experiences at any given moment. An adrenaline rush can mean physical ailment or excitement for something upcoming. The choice is ours and depending on that choice we will create positive or negative momentum in our lives.

Every suggestion we accept by the mind or body makes the next suggestion that aligns with it more likely to be accepted. So, if we continue to perceive our bodies as being against us, we will continue to be in competition with it rather than cooperate with it. Therefore we must be open-minded and open-hearted each and every day. Health anxiety will not kill you, or else it would have done so by now. These symptoms that you experience may feel real and seem to connect to other physical problems but in reality, they are simply connected to suppressed feelings and emotions. As we open ourselves up to understanding more deeply the roots of these symptoms we can begin doing something we haven't done for ourselves in a long time. We can begin to forgive ourselves.

Forgiving yourself logically is not enough, you must own it and believe in the forgiveness. Only then will your subconscious mind get the message. Forgive yourself for believing what you did in the past, for thinking that fear and worry were some types of protective responses you needed to stand by daily, and for making mistakes. Forgiveness is one of those things that unexpected sources of support can support you in understanding more deeply and accepting into your heart if you are open to it. You may find yourself randomly crying out of deep clarity while sitting on a bench one day; at this moment you should put the tissues aside and allow your body to purge itself of your deeply held fears and angers. These are the types of spontaneous experiences that add to your new insights. So approach each day with a willingness to understand more deeply, replace your fear with self-love, and connect your desire with your feelings. Once balance has been found on the inside, it will show up on the outside and be your greatest cheerleader each and every day during this healing journey.

Mapping

Mapping will be one of the most useful skill sets that you use daily. In fact, mapping has the potential of doing several things for your health anxiety healing, such as:

- Being the bridge between the subconscious mind and the conscious mind
- Creating new and more understanding associations around bodily sensations
- Building trust in leaving the body to its own form of intelligence to heal what needs healing

Upon writing this book my guided mapping practice on YouTube had reached over 140,000 views and I highly recommend using part 1 and part 2 regularly through this stage of the healing process. Just place the keywords 'Mapping The Anxiety Guy' onto the search bar and begin. However, I will also provide a script for you here to memorize or even record into your very own mapping session that you may follow daily if you choose to. The reason I'm doing this is because anytime an instruction comes from your own voice it is that much more powerful since you view yourself as the greatest authority there is.

Mapping will help you to turn off the secondary fear response when you feel a bodily symptom of anxiety. Yes, you may still feel the sudden or lingering types of bodily sensations of anxiety, but upon bringing conscious awareness to it you will find that you are no longer placing more fear on top of the original fear. This is what mapping is meant to do. It's meant to help you to reconnect with whatever it is your body is doing and to keep your emotions at bay. By neutralizing our response to the original reptilian-led fear response, we can stop the cycle of fear – adrenaline – fear. When done regularly, this mindfulness practice will begin to heal you of your fear of uncertainty around your bodily sensations while no longer necessitating your need for control. To calm your nervous system and bring safety perceptions while in your comfort zones isn't enough, that same feeling and perception must be present in times of inner or situational challenges as well. Therefore mapping must be a part of your daily health anxiety healing routine. Let's get to the script, and I promise you that reading this script into a simple USB microphone prior to listening and using it daily will do wonders for your health anxiety.

Mapping Meditation script:

Take a few moments to get comfortable, either sitting or lying down, as you give yourself full permission to be one with this exercise, to release yourself of the things you have to do, and the things that have happened. Just be present for a few moments.

As you close your eyes and take a deep breath, notice how good that feels. And as you take another deep breath, release yourself of more and more tension.

Turn your focus to your feet. As you focus on your feet, you're non-judgmental. It's not a good feeling. It's not a bad feeling. It's just your feet. Turn your focus to your stomach area. And as you focus on your stomach area, it's not a good feeling. It's not a bad feeling. It's just your stomach, doing what it needs to do.

As you turn your focus to your forehead. And as you focus on your forehead, you are non-judgmental. You accept whatever is there. It's not a good feeling. It's not a bad feeling. It just is.

And within this fully accepting you. You focus on your arms. And as you focus on your arms, it's not a good feeling. It's not a bad feeling. It just is. As you are non-judgmental. As you are fully accepting of whatever is there right now. You trust.

As you turn your focus to the top part of your legs, your quadriceps, it's not a good feeling. It's not a bad feeling. It just is. And you fully accept whatever is there right now. As you build more and more trust in your body.

As you turn your focus to your chest area. It's not a good feeling. And it's not a bad feeling. Whatever is there right now is, and you release the need to control it. You release the need to have certainty over it and you trust in your body and you fully accept what is there, right now in your chest area.

As you turn your focus to your neck, and as you focus on your neck area. It's not a good feeling. And it's not a bad feeling. Whatever is there is there and you let go of the need to control it. You let go of the need to have certainty around it. And you trust and you trust in your body to heal itself the way it was meant to do so.

As you turn your attention to your face and all the parts of your face. It's not a good feeling, not a bad feeling. You are non-judgmental as to the feeling as you just are there with whatever is. You're not trying to alter it, not trying to change any part of it. But be one with it. As you build your trust in your body, as you turn your focus to your entire body now.

It's not a good feeling, it's not a bad feeling, it just is. And moment by moment, it becomes easier and easier to let go and trust in your body to heal itself, to have faith in what is to come, and to know that you don't have to have all the answers.

At this moment, you are one with your body. You are allowing whatever your body wants to do, to do it. You are not analyzing, you are letting go. You are trusting and giving your body permission to heal itself now. As you focus on your entire body, notice how it's okay to let go just a little bit more. Notice that it's okay to trust just a little bit more.

And there may be a part of you that says it's uncertain. And to that you say, 'I trust in uncertainty'. As you non-judgmentally are here with your body. It's not a good feeling. It's not a bad feeling. It just is.

You feel yourself getting lighter and lighter with every moment that passes and that's okay. Believe me, that's okay. As you remind yourself that I deserve to be healed. I deserve to be healed. I deserve to be healed.

And as you sit or lay down for the next few moments, you allow yourself to let go even more.

And the more you let go, the closer you get to who you're meant to be.

Light, happy, trusting, faithful, and empowered. Give yourself full permission to just be, just be, just be, because it's safe to do so.

As you focus back on your fee. Notice how much easier it is to just let go of needing all the answers. It's not a good feeling and it's not a bad feeling, it just is.

As you focus on your calves, non-judgmentally looking at your calves from the outside, it just is and I let go of whatever is going on there right now. As you focus on your knees and your quads, think to yourself, 'I let go and I trust in my body'.

As you focus on your torso, and you focus on your waist, I let go and trust in my body.

As you focus on your chest area, your shoulders, and your arms, I let go and trust in my body.

As you focus on your neck area, I let go and trust in my body.

As you focus on your face, all the way up to your forehead and the top of your head, I let go and trust in my body.

And as you sit or lay comfortably and light, you are with your body now, non-judgmental. And you are just being one with it. Allowing it to do what it needs to do.

As you are safe. And the more you let go, the safer you become. And the more you trust in your body, the safer you become. And you are healed.

As you deserve this healing, stay with this feeling now. This feeling of letting go. This feeling of peace. This feeling of being non-judgmental, this feeling of tremendous faith. This feeling of deservingness.

As you say this day will be a great day. As I count to five you'll begin wiggling your toes and your fingers and when I get to five, your eyes will open. You will have a tremendous sense of lightness and you will accept this lightness, you will not question it. You will allow your system to process what you did and you will accept it fully. 1, 2, 3, 4, and 5. Open up your eyes. Notice how good you feel and remember that you are more than your anxiety. Enjoy the day.

There you have it, one of the most important skill sets to use no matter what stage in the health anxiety healing journey you are on. Even during my maintenance stage now post health anxiety, I still use Mapping regularly. If you're wondering when would be the best time to use Mapping, I would say in the evening or right before bed to limit the amount of worry you do as much as possible. As you can see, the relationship building process between the conscious mind and the subconscious body is vital for achieving optimal overall health. Soon you will be in control of the inner processes you can have control over and let go of the external ones you can't have control over.

Chapter 5:
The True Meaning of Your Bodily Symptoms

With health anxiety what we think our bodily symptoms mean isn't what they really mean. In this chapter, we're going to take major steps forward in understanding the body and its messages better. After years of research and a keen interest in decoding what the body is telling us, I've recognized that these symptoms are caused by the body's natural response to unresolved conflict and past trauma, which then translates into warning signs based around protection. The reactions we have to the unconscious triggers that ignite these bodily symptoms keep us within the habitual loop of fear-confirmed threat escalation of fear. The body is 100% memory, and often we're not sure of what memories connect to the bodily symptoms until we start paying closer attention to those very moments when the body starts screaming out. I don't believe it is necessary to know which traumas are connected to which symptoms (although it can help in the emotional reframing process of completing or healing trauma), but I do believe that the physical purging effect of suppressed feelings, labels, and emotions is a necessary part of the healing process. This outcome can be connected to a predetermined practice of some sort or can spontaneously show up at any given moment. Breath work (specifically alongside utilizing the language of color), inner child work, exposure work, chair therapy/coaching, hypnosis, inner child-directed affirmation work coupled with touch on specific parts of the body, and imagery work all have great potential to create this purging effect and I would connect this to being the 'deeper work' I referred to earlier.

As our conscious awareness grows and we become more willing to understand what the body is trying to tell us, we begin sensing what sort of meanings we've unconsciously placed on external things due to past experiences that were out of our control. The science of epigenetics tells us that trauma has the potential to create biological change that can last for many generations. This translates into the understanding that even when we simply witness a trauma during the early years of our lives, it can physically and emotionally affect future generations. Therefore, health anxiety and anxiety in general within your family tree will end with you.

You are the one called to do the deeper work necessary to reverse anxiety, and you are the one that will live with a deep sense of fulfillment for the rest of your life knowing you've achieved something deeply rewarding for your entire ancestry line.

Commonly, however, we are afraid of letting go of our symptoms since it feels like we now have a growing relationship with them. Of course, at a conscious level, you may think 'I'll do anything to be rid of this feeling'. However, the unconscious parts of you may feel like you'd be losing more than you'd be gaining should they disappear. Ridding ourselves of our symptoms would mean changing the meaning of our past traumas and releasing the suppressed emotions within that part of the body. To the subconscious mind and body, this would mean that you would have to relearn what life truly means, which in turn would negate all the habits we've come to grow comfortable with all these years. The subconscious mind is certainly open to this, but would rather not relearn things all over again. It likes to keep things as they are. And if fear and anxiety have been at the forefront of our minds and bodies for all these years and we've survived, it initially wouldn't understand the reasons for changing who we've become, and as a result will create a host of barriers as to why it's not the right time, why change is too difficult, etc., to prevent it.

Familiarity quite often overpowers logic.

Logic becomes our initial response or tool that we use to help ourselves understand that our symptoms are not life-threatening. I believe logic provides temporary help at best to relieve the symptoms and turn our attention toward safety perceptions. The subconscious mind has certain languages that it uses to communicate with our conscious minds and we can use these same languages to help it understand what's true for us today. Some of these are:

- **Mental movies and visualization** (add somatic engagement to this process for even greater change, as I show you on my YouTube channel). – The greater the emotional arousal in any given situation, the bigger and brighter the mental movie. We unconsciously visualize all the time and we have done so in a way that has brought on chronic anxiety. We are simply reversing the process when we consciously imagine what we want rather than unconsciously imagine the worst that could happen (as mentioned earlier in the book).

- **Color breathing** – Your first language out of the womb was color. As you grew, you began the process of connecting some colors as being your safety colors and some as your threatening colors. Taking time throughout the day to breathe in your safety color and breathe out your fear-based colors will communicate the perception of safety within the environment you are in, along with everything within that environment.

- **Mantras** – A mantra is a single or group of words that empower the speaker. Ancient healing and manifesting methods around Shamanism, for example, show us the power of mantras in inducing a trance-like or disassociated state. When we are in a deeper trance, we are no longer overthinking but rather sending clear signals of what it is we desire. One example of a mantra that I use is using the words 'Here, Now.' 'Here' on the inhale, and 'now' on the exhale. I won't pay attention to the number of repetitions I do with this mantra but instead focus on letting go completely of whatever feelings come up as I continue with this mantra.

These are just a few examples of methods we can integrate into our daily lives to help clear our bodies of any excess emotional weight we are carrying. Suppression turns into expression as our bodily symptoms begin to fade and trust is built in the direction we're headed. However, we must also understand that clearing one particular negative thought or bodily symptom won't resolve the underlying cause of the symptoms. Therefore, our focus must turn from the physical aspect of the symptom to the emotional one. While healing we cry out of expression, out of faith and joy rather than through self-victimization.

When we can redirect our focus in this way we are captaining our own ship, we are navigating the body out of the troubled waters of the past and into the calm seas of the present. Our future is no longer decided by what happened to us in the past, but rather our future is being created by how we decide to perceive what happened to us in the past. When it comes to past trauma, I initially often ask my clients what they felt during the moment of trauma. Their initial heart-led answer is commonly 'afraid, I felt afraid.' This is commonly followed by bewilderment, feeling more frightened, angry, and then guilty. Imagine at a young age not having the cognitive resources and possibly courage to express these feelings toward an authority figure, but rather suppressing them deep into the largest part of your subconscious mind, your body. Seeing the compounding effect of such experiences throughout a lifetime, it is no surprise to many that they're in the state of anxiety that they are currently in. Also, seeing the past experiences from the perspective of the experienced adult often neglects the fact that the experience was, in fact, overwhelming to the younger child. We must be very careful not to downplay the experiences we had as children and neglect the overwhelming perceptions we may have had while we were children, no matter what the experience was. To downplay the inner child's perceptions is to reject the need to express what has been suppressed emotionally in that part of the body. As a child, you craved appreciation and acceptance more than anything, and now as an adult, it is the time to give back what you didn't fully receive when you were young.

Fear looks for more fear, which creates a perpetual cycle of being afraid of the very next moment. Health anxiety sufferers have a challenging time seeing the positive possibility in things and return to a default state to protect themselves from a new experience that may heighten their bodily symptoms and spur on a host of catastrophic ideas.

The biggest problem with health anxiety isn't so much the discomfort of the bodily symptoms as it is the rigidity which we begin adopting into our lives. Our minds become less and less flexible in thought and our bodies stiffen up, which causes shallow breathing and leads to muscle tension, which then can lead to hypertension.

Often, we hold onto our pain as survival stories to share with others in order to receive something in return. However, when trauma is reframed, when the body has released itself of these suppressed feelings and labels, the stories we tell others are stories around defiance, not acceptance. To defy your old core beliefs would be to believe in a new story around what took place in your life during childhood. Tell yourself a different story with a sense of certainty and you'll create a new meaning and feeling toward the experience. With that said I want to dive deep into some of the physical symptoms due to anxiety that you may be experiencing in your life right now. We'll be looking at the main emotional components that lead to the bodily anxiety symptom.

I'd like you to explore the emotional connections to your physical symptoms as if looking to truly understand your bodily messages for the first time. Have an open mind and enter this stage of this book with a desire for deeper reflection and understanding. We will start with what I believe is the most common anxiety symptom around today, dizziness and depersonalization.

Dizziness and Depersonalization.

Often, health anxiety sufferers explain their dizziness as an off-balance feeling coupled with brain fog and an inability to concentrate on one thing. Depersonalization can sometimes be challenging to differentiate from the dizziness but is known as a feeling of being out of touch with reality, out of touch with your senses, and feeling like you're living in a bubble. The entire experience can cause tremendous mental, emotional and physical strain, and often health anxiety sufferers do every test their physician recommends without ever finding a physical cause. While resting, these symptoms can be much more noticeable, which motivates the person to stay busy and therefore distracted. This can be coupled with a feeling of moving through the world feeling numb, which in fact means that you are being chemically protected from further feelings of overwhelm.

Here are some of the potential mind body connection causes:

Over-breathing: As much as we are focused on the emotional causes of these anxiety symptoms, it's important to recognize how those emotional causes connect to physiological habits, in this case connected to our breathing patterns. When over-breathing, more CO_2 (carbon dioxide) is getting released from the body than the body produces. Blood vessels constrict, sending less oxygen to the brain and other extremities as the acidity in the blood changes. A few signs of over-breathing are:

- Taking more than 14 breaths per minute
- Chest breathing
- Air hunger (gasping for air)

Fixes for over-breathing:

- Breathe through your nose rather than your mouth
- Remind yourself to breathe 'low and slow' throughout the day, meaning diaphragmatic breathing at a speed that equals 4 seconds in and 4 seconds out
- Less panic, more guidance toward your body when you sense you are over-breathing. This shift

from competing with your body to cooperating with it will lead to more clarity.

Fear of change:

A recurring theme for people going through dizziness and depersonalization. The fear of change may have been installed into you by an authority figure that didn't necessarily feel comfortable with the way you did things as a child, and wanted to pull you into their habits and views of the world instead. Remember, to your subconscious mind familiarity equals safety, but at the same time familiarity also produces similar feelings and symptoms. When we begin seeing change in a positive light we start moving away from rigid thinking and toward flexible thinking. This is a perceptual shift that must be coupled with behavioral shifts, to have the courage to do what is in line with the new ideas you want to adopt into your life. As the fear of change turns into valuing change and understanding that at a fundamental level everything changes anyway, life will begin introducing us to new people, experiences, and feelings. As you open up to the world, so will you give your body the permission to let go of old perceptions of yourself which will go a long way toward healing your dizziness and depersonalization.

Making peace with peace:

Slowing down and intending to relax often has a negative association connected to it for health anxiety sufferers. The practice of meditation, for example, can be a daunting exercise that we soon give up on simply because the idea of letting go scares us back into those familiar stress hormones we've become so acquainted with. When we make peace with peace, we give the body a chance to recover and heal itself since I truly believe that a body at peace cannot manifest dis-ease.

The first step is to see beyond your core beliefs that say slowing down is laziness, self-care is selfishness, and inner peace leads to being unproductive.

Reflection leads to higher levels of consciousness that will lead to opportunities for change. Wherever these old limiting core beliefs came from, they must be reversed. Your parents did the best they could with the information they got from their parents. Bless them for looking out for us and teaching us what they believed was the best approach to life. However, you must come into your own now and realize that you are neither your mom's, dad's, nor any other authority figures' beliefs.

When you make peace with peace you are replacing a frantic and dizzying world with one that is in balance with the laws of nature. Have you ever noticed how much you can learn about yourself simply by walking alone in a naturalistic environment with the intent to understand yourself and life more deeply? When peace shows up, let it in, allow it to stick around. Don't become threatened by it simply because it feels different. Rather, take time to get to know peace and your body will certainly thank you for it.

The inability to focus on one thing:

Scattered and flighty thinking goes hand in hand with dizziness and depersonalization. There is an inability to focus on one thing which brings me back to the challenge of meditation, as well as the focus on solely the breath, which becomes a great challenge. When you find that you are beginning to strengthen your ability to focus your attention and energy on one thing for an extended period, your inner resources won't be working so hard to decode so many pieces of information coming from the outside world. This gives your body a real break and allows for you to get clear on what the next step is on the ladder of your own healing journey. When you've mastered your ability to focus on one thing for as long as you prefer, you will find that you feel more rested throughout the day. To master this, I recommend the meditation practice starting with:

- Laying down with your hand on your stomach so that you are breathing from a place of 'low and slow.'
- Breathing in for 4 seconds through your nose.
- Breathing out for 6 seconds through your mouth
- Continue for only 2 minutes, 3 times per day

When your focus wants to turn to other things, just bring it right back to your breath. As you get better at keeping your focus on one thing you may increase your lying meditation time as you wish.

Lump in the throat feeling (Globus Hystericus).

This feels like a golf ball is stuck in your throat and you feel the need to constantly clear your throat (clicking sounds in the throat while clearing are also common). Often, eating and drinking can be challenging, and we can become frustratingly obsessed with this symptom. As tension builds, this lump in the throat feeling becomes more persistent as we focus more on ridding ourselves of the symptom rather than recognizing which suppressed feelings and thoughts may be causing it. See if you can relate to these potential causes:

An inability to express ideas and feelings:

I find that many people experiencing Globus don't feel like they have the true support they need. They're looking for others to be able to relate and understand their inner pain, and because they don't have that connection can only suppress their inner challenges (and even future goals) further. When we feel connected and heard we give ourselves further permission and courage to express. When we feel alone in our suffering, we feel trapped, and since our throat is our avenue of expression and creativity, we find ourselves living in our comfort zones more and exploring new ideas, experiences, and places less.

Swallowed anger:

This suppressed anger commonly connects to blame. We feel like someone, or a group of people could have done things differently, maybe could have cared more, loved more, and so our blame runs deep. We carry this blame and anger in our throat areas which tends to come out in our present experiences and is often unjustified. Like an overflowing cup, if the roots of our anger which have plenty to do with broken past relationships aren't resolved we will continue to feel the tension in our throats. However, when we can bring resolve to our suppressed anger and communicate our thoughts to the person or people we are most angry at, more often than not the symptom will subside.

Stifled creativity:

Here there is a feeling of being unable to presently live up to the creative potential we know we have within us. There is a feeling of being held back, and please understand that I myself have been through this chapter also. The emotional components to your physical symptoms are to be reflected upon and understood more deeply, these are not meant to bring you down further. It is not until we admit to ourselves what's truly taking place at a deeper level that we begin to heal, and healing can be messy at times yes, but it is meant to be this way for reasons you will only understand later in your life. I would wholeheartedly recommend that if you feel like you are unable to bring out your artistic and creative sides currently, you stop convincing yourself that these symptoms must be gone prior to acting. Do not wait for the right time, the right time is now. And in small daily doses tap back into your creative sides however they want to show up. Some people want to get back to singing, dancing, painting, even philosophizing can be seen as a creative act of sorts. Maybe your creativity wants to arise as a part of your career choice. If you are led in this direction this is great as well, and you must have the courage to follow what feels right to you now. The lump in the throat symptom and holding back go hand in hand. It will subside as you become more expressive in every way, especially creatively. Remember, expression in one area of our lives will trickle into the next.

Headache and Head Pressure.

For most health anxiety sufferers this symptom feels more like tension headaches than migraines. A feeling of heaviness, fullness, an ache if you will, but rarely going beyond this. Some of the emotionally led reasons for these tension headaches you will connect with immediately, and some may take further reflection. Either way, it's vitally important to understand that when it comes to this and your other bodily symptoms, your old approach will only get you so far. We must begin opening ourselves up to ideas connected to these symptoms that you haven't considered yet. Only then will we be able to move into a world where the driving force for your life is your intuition, your trust in yourself and life, along with love.

Excessive mental activity:

Yes, we all think, some people more consciously than others. But there are those in the health anxiety world that obsess and believe they are in fact thinking. Obsessing isn't thinking as much as it is reacting and replaying the ideas your protective sides want you to replay. I've found that when a person resorts more often to solving their problems through their mental faculties over their intuitive one's, stagnant energy becomes stuck in the head area. Like a balloon that gets deflated when the air is taken out, so do the tension headaches subside when we respond to our problems and challenges differently. No, not every problem needs a solution from you, and inaction can be as powerful as action for health anxiety.

This demands an ability to leave something alone at times, including your tension headaches. It's easy to revert to a pill to stop the tension, it's more challenging to sit with it and observe it. I would suggest doing what feels challenging until it no longer does. Leaving things alone, in this case the bodily symptoms perpetuated by anxiety, is the goal for us. It proves that safety has been updated as a new perception in the present and future. This feeling of inaction doesn't appear instantly; however, it takes time, patience, and continued guidance toward a body that is still stuck in its old associations. However, these tension headaches more often than not disappear when our mindset towards them changes, and you have the power to make this change starting today. The act of inaction must be intuitively led, however, and would go into the category of 'responding' (the act you choose in the moment of fear).

A lack of trust:

As mentioned earlier in this book, trust has the power to create a domino effect. When trust is built in one area of life, say your relationships, you are much more open to trusting in other areas (like in your body). This is because the brain learns through experience. These new experiences connect to new feelings in the present moment which lead to new core beliefs. Trust is the necessary ingredient not only to eliminate these tension headaches, but to give your life a sense of flow. It eventually feels like you are no longer stuck in traffic, moving forward slightly just before you slam the brakes again. The path ahead becomes smooth, and the way to trust is to open yourself up to new interpretations.

When you are given the opportunity to interpret an experience differently, no matter how awkward it feels, become open to it. Don't force yourself to accept it, just be open to it.

Cognitive dissonance is a feeling that goes against a belief you hold, and therefore labelling it as being wrong. New feelings and ideas are not wrong, they're just new, and until you can begin adopting these new ideas we will continue to get the same physical results we're getting. The mind and body are one, there is no separation. What the mind believes the body believes, and vice versa. A lack of trust in yourself, the safety within this world, and within your relationships may be the cause of your tension headaches and if this is the case, your intuitive sense will ask you to explore this area more deeply until change is effectively brought forward.

Self-criticism:

This cause was brought forward by Louis Hay, a metaphysical teacher and wonderful human being who helped to re-shape how we saw ourselves and the world. In my years of working with over 10,000+ people to heal from various forms of anxiety, I've rarely recognized these mental and emotional connections to various physical symptoms and sensations to be wrong. When it comes to self-criticism I believe these traits were consciously and unconsciously picked up from our parents and other authority figures. The demands of us when we were children to not only do things their way but to make sure life was lived a certain way turned us into rigid beings. This rigidity leaves no room for creativity or flexibility in feeling, thought, or action. It's easier to criticize ourselves than it is to mentally reward ourselves. Society favors the people that 'get the job done' so to speak, but what use is it to get the job done and lose touch with ourselves in the process? How much punishment can a vehicle, for instance, take before it can no longer run? Love is truly a healing force, the greatest one in fact, which creates a heart-led electromagnetic frequency that positively affects everyone around you.

There can be no love if there is no support, and support starts with supporting ourselves through the good and bad.

It's best to reflect on your level of self-criticism and see if this way of internally dialoguing with your inner child has become a pattern. If it is in fact the case, bodily contact will be your best friend. More specifically, self-hugs. You know that amazing feeling we get when someone hugs us and tells us everything is going to be alright? Well, why not begin making self-hugs a consistent thing you do for your inner child when he or she needs it? How about right now in fact, give yourself a self-hug and reconnect with your compassionate parts once again. Apologize to your body for treating it so randomly in the last few years and promise it that inner peace and self-love will be at the forefront of all your inner dialogues from now on.

Heart palpitations:

Within the symptom of heart palpitations, I will only go into the connection it has to the past replaying in some way in the present. Heart palpitations are scary, let's not kid ourselves. The idea that our hearts could potentially let us down can create a storm of other catastrophic ideas to form into feelings and core beliefs. Upon initially experiencing this symptom a person can potentially allow all their focus to turn on keeping an eye out for the next one. This can drain our spiritual and physical energies and leave us in financial debt, nutritional debt, and sleep debt solely since because we are out of touch with the external world and our internal needs.

Once you've gotten your heart checked out and have gotten the 'all clear' it's important to turn your focus toward the mental and emotional causes.

There is initially a surprised feeling when the doctor says there's nothing wrong structurally with your heart. I understand, I've been there. But that surprise should turn to reflection soon enough. When you begin reflecting on what it was within your thought processes or within the environment that may have spurred on the heart palpitations, we can begin understanding why the subconscious mind body felt the need to react this way. Sometimes it's the amount of people, or an abundance of the colour red or black (trauma colours for most people), or it's also possible that your imagination got the best of you, and you began unconsciously painting a picture of doom and gloom around a future experience. This kind of deeper reflection will help to rebuild our relationships with our bodies and our memories since it's memory that spurred on a need to physically react this way. As you can see as well, when you do something different, anything really in the present when these symptoms arise, you are literally re-writing what your past experiences mean. A trauma can turn into just another experience if you can find it within yourself to speak up in moments when you want to shy away from a conversation. Or let's say you're headed into a workshop and your instincts, which are of course led by past memory, pull you toward sitting all the way in the back. Instead, you sit in the middle (or front if you're really feeling defiant) and go through the entire workshop with nothing more than a physical hiccup. You have shown your inner child that everything within that environment that was seen, heard, felt, smelled, and tasted is of the safe variety. Therefore, the trauma connected to the experience when other kids were laughing at you in your old elementary school classroom becomes nothing more than a learning lesson.

We have the potential to encode a new meaning over our past by imagining a different outcome over what took place (reframing), or by enacting a different action in the present.

The number of repetitions it would take to change the meaning of an experience isn't of our concern here. This isn't within our control. But what is, is what we do. Sometimes one new defiant emotional reframing process (under The Anxiety Guy YouTube Channel's 'Reframing' playlist, or my digital programs) or behavioral experience is enough to change the connection to the past, other times it takes longer, which can test our persistence and faith. When these heart palpitations subside, you will truly know that the body feels safe again with what it's doing and where it is. When this happens we will feel a sense of openness toward people and things we were closed off toward before, and life will have a different flavour to it. This is a well-deserved moment, and another self-hug would be more than appreciated by your own inner child.

Shaking and or muscle twitching:

Often when health anxiety sufferers feel this symptom they go straight to Dr. Google and connect these symptoms to having ALS. They begin not only convincing themselves, but others around them that they could be suffering from a life-threatening disease. Because the feelings connected to these ideas are so intense, there is a potential of turning them into a core belief which would mean that only a new idea connected to the same level of emotional intensity would have the potential to overturn the belief.

Until a health anxiety sufferer is certain about the new emotionally-led causes to their anxiety symptoms they will continue telling themselves the same old self-sabotaging stories.

You cannot be confident in the idea that your bodily symptoms are connected to memory and a subconscious mind and body that has stored the interpretations made from you and your family lines from the past, you must be certain about it. When this level of certainty arises, disinterest around the old ways of treating your anxiety symptoms arises, which as well opens the flood gates to freedom.

Fight fatigue.

These particular symptoms connect to a need and established patterns to fight off and fight for pretty much everything. A fight for a better parking space, fighting off your child's bullies at his school, fighting for that raise you deserve at work, etc. There seems to be an established belief that if you don't fight, you'll get left behind. You may have difficulty slowing down and practicing mindfulness, for example, since your mind is always rushing to what needs to be fought for next. Sometimes in life it's necessary to fight for the truth, what you believe in, or for others. However, these moments are few and far between. This fighting mindset has more to do with the fear of losing control than anything else, which in turn is connected to a deep need for certainty. Without certainty in all things there can only be uncertainty, and uncertainty doesn't sit well within health anxiety individuals who are dealing with this symptom.

Hoping not to lose out on something.

An aspect that goes hand in hand with fighting is the hope that something, or a group of things you deem as valuable isn't taken from you. Your job, your friendships, your vehicle, your reputation even. You may be holding onto life with such a tight grip that it becomes impossible to see the positive potential in anything anymore. Fighting to keep something the way it is is an unconscious survival based reaction, whereas looking to create something from where you currently are is a conscious response. The latter doesn't come easy, nor does it feel natural, at least at the beginning of this kind of change work. This pattern must come to the awareness of a health anxiety sufferer or else they may conclude that this approach is normal for themselves and everyone else. We become shocked that others don't experience the same thing that we do on a daily basis. The next time you catch yourself working so hard not to lose something or lose out to something, remind yourself that you also have the option to create something new instead. If you're afraid to lose your job for example, don't look to preserve an outdated identity for the sake of a paycheque and a few co-workers. Instead, begin working on building your creative side business, and let the empowered and excited identity connected to this endeavor flow toward other aspects of your life. Afraid to lose a friend? Head to a café and spark a conversation with a stranger instead. Create, create, create, challenge yourself within your limits often (these limits will enhance over time). The more comfortable you get with these new experiences, the more open-minded you will become, which will in turn allow health anxiety to subside.

Stomach and digestive issues:

One more time I will emphasize the importance of meeting with a physician prior regarding the symptoms you are concerned over, prior to taking on the journey of clearing out negative emotional blocks that are affecting your physical body. However, in my experience any idea that is held firmly within the subconscious mind of the individual will also rule the life of that person. Hence, even surgery wouldn't be enough to eliminate the core beliefs that are affecting the human body; instead the messages of guilt, unforgiveness, rage, fear, etc will only travel to another part of the body. In all aspects of our lives this subconscious mind body is constantly at work looking to accomplish and bring to the forefront the conscious, subconscious, and subliminal wishes of the individual. Therefore, we must begin seeing the human body as a reflection of the soul, the subconscious mind led by the inner child's perceptions. Because only then can we truly begin seeing what's taking place below the level of our conscious awareness.

For years my digestive issues created stomach bloating, gastrointestinal problems, constipation and more. It wasn't until I began targeting the areas that I will show you here that I truly felt like my self- care work was truly focused.

Nervousness and hesitation about the future.

There is a hesitation here about what's to come. When thinking about the future (because uncertainty doesn't sit very well with health anxiety sufferers) you may be finding it difficult to connect optimistic ideas and mental movies to what is to come. The problem with this is that if there is no consciously led direction, the subconscious mind and body will revert to what's been practiced the most often, along with what came first in the person's life. So, if there was pessimism, doubt, conflict in the house growing up, this will be the baseline in terms of what the subconscious mind will bring to fruition for the future. Not knowing an outcome to something doesn't mean you have to 'wait and see' what will happen. This is a survival reaction in plain view. The subconscious mind is open to direction by the conscious mind while simultaneously being okay with what it already predicts for the future. Pay very close attention to the words that come out of your mouth which follow the words 'I am,' since 'I am' is an identity statement that will determine which persona parts you enact throughout the day and what your future will look like. Nervousness and hesitation don't have to turn into pessimism and hoping for the best. It's just an inner child reaction to something unfamiliar, and remember that the power lies in guiding the inner child in ways that feel like the message is getting across.

Difficulty digesting and turning new ideas into beliefs.

A new idea will only be a fleeting thing if it's not coupled with a certain degree of certainty and emotion. Following these components, enacting the new idea consistently becomes absolutely essential in order for the old to be replaced with the new. We fear the consequences of adopting a new belief mainly because of what people may think about us and what we'd have to give up for it. For example, every health anxiety sufferer reading this right now has the potential to see their bodily symptoms as something different than how they've been interpreting them up to this point. But what if things get worse before they get better? This isn't so much a conscious idea as it is unconsciously right there in the background of our minds. It's like preparing to go for a swim in a cold lake of water when you're so used to warm showers back home. The moment your feet touch the edge of the water on the lake you feel the mental and physiological shock wave go through your body saying, 'NO DON'T DO IT!' This reaction isn't so much because the water is a threat of some sort, in actuality there is enormous benefit in swimming in a fresh cold lake of water. But because it's not a familiar act, we begin the process of convincing ourselves why we shouldn't jump in. We don't consider the benefits, only the risks. That is, until we've had enough of our old ways and the results they've been producing.

No one will create the kind of change they desire until they've hit rock bottom.

Once we understand the blocks to why we feel so challenged to accept a new idea, even if it is more beneficial to us, we can begin unravelling the old ideas and beliefs we've held onto for so long. Health anxiety isn't something that showed up out of the blue for you. It's a manifestation of years and years of unconsciously deciphering experiences and data through your 5 senses. Adopting a new idea into your life takes courage, a willingness to step out of your comfort zones, and an acknowledgement that it's necessary for the future you that you are creating.

Suppressed rage.

You'll notice that I haven't used the word anger in connection to this symptom, but rather used the word 'rage.' This rage more often than not has something to do with feeling like you've been done wrong in some way, and you never deserved what happened to you. Rage within the subconscious mind is central toward more deeply understanding our psycho somatic reactions. We often sense this rage throughout the entire day and allow it to be expressed toward situations in the present, often unjustifiably. Other people today pay the price for years of suppressing this rage, which often has everything to do with an inability to please parents, unable to do things perfectly, and overall not being where others told you that you need to be at this juncture in your life (financially or otherwise).

Self-compassion and reflection are key here.

As mentioned earlier in this book, in order to update an old negative emotion into a new one it must be met with a new emotion that matches the intensity of the old emotion. For example, the rage can turn into excitement over this healing journey that you are on. And once you begin recognizing each reason for why you are excited for this journey, the emotion of excitement and anticipation will only grow stronger over time. When you can do this repeatedly, the meaning over your past traumas have the potential to change from being traumatic to an experience that showed you things no one or nothing ever could. This is less about positive thinking and more about understanding how to communicate with our own inner child. I often refer to my present life as being the 'After Life' when doing YouTube live streams with many of my subscribers there. I explain to them how different a person I am now and how I see the world today compared to during my health anxiety days. The suppressed rage has calmed within me, I have found inner peace, and with it have met with experiences I would have never met had I still been stuck in my health anxiety patterns.

I most likely haven't been able to touch on all the bodily anxiety symptoms you may be experiencing in the moment. However, I hope I have been able to open your eyes to some of the root causes that you may not have considered before. It is not the traumatic experience itself that gets stored in the body for later recall and hopefully resolution, it is the interpretation made by the individual's own perceptual system that determines what an experience means. Hence, any experience can be deemed a trauma from childhood, and with the meaning of trauma we can store a host of negative labels toward ourselves and the world. This is an important point that you must reflect on more deeply, since more often than not I hear people say, 'I never experienced trauma in my childhood.' When I began helping them to change the meaning of trauma they began understanding how their systems may have accumulated certain beliefs and self-labels throughout the years.

You are not broken; you are just bent.

Through this book our goal together must be to unbend you in mind, body, spirit as we re-learn the meaning of things over again (including love). When something angers you in the present you now can let it be, imagine that, letting things be. What would be the outcome of this new response? Re-programming, that's what would take place. In time this inaction (should you be intuitively pulled to respond to a situation this way) doesn't mean further suppression but rather emotional neutrality toward petty things you gave up too much energy toward before. Remember, your life force is finite. You decide where your energy will be placed from now on and you have no time for gossip, drama, or other life sucking experiences. Your energy must now be focused on working with the body and inner child to bring about mental neutrality. Since it's neutrality that opens the pathway toward inner peace and happiness. At this point we no longer need the new shoes, the car, a bigger house etc to feel a sense of happiness. We start simplifying our lives and with this simplification we start ridding ourselves of all unnecessary things in our lives.

An external detox takes place alongside the internal one.

We spend less time with certain friends and family members without any guilt whatsoever. We start eliminating things in our house we never use but only bought due to the dopamine spike we felt at that very moment while shopping. We are no longer shackled to a system that tells us that suffering is inevitable unless you buy our product or do as we say. Healing health anxiety influences every aspect of our lives as empowerment sets in deeply. It's no longer a feeling that comes and goes but rather a personal trait that fits with our new beliefs and identity.

Take a moment now to simply reflect on the most important lessons you gathered from this chapter before moving on. You will never regret the love you show for yourself, but you and the world will only benefit from it.

Chapter 6:
The Setbacks: Frustration and Self-Blame

You may find yourself feeling frustrated while healing your health anxiety. The most obvious of frustrations that we tend to encounter is when we continue to feel the bodily symptoms and emotions even after much inner work. The new perceptions and understandings may be coming to the surface, but they simply don't seem to cause a physiological shift. I understand deeply this see-saw-like process within the healing pathway, which is why I find it's important to elaborate and help you understand these two conflicting inner systems better:

The parasympathetic nervous system (PNS) controls homeostasis (meaning inner balance and a body at rest). The sympathetic nervous system (SNS) controls the body's responses to a perceived threat and is responsible for the 'fight or flight' system. Both PNS and SNS comprise the autonomic nervous system (ANS) and are responsible for the involuntary functions of the human body. With sympathetic nervous responses, the body speeds up, tenses up, and becomes highly alert, causing the functions that are not essential for survival to shut down. Here are a few of the bodily responses that arise when the sympathetic nervous system is activated:

- An increase in the rate and constriction of the heart
- Dilation of bronchial tubes in the lungs and of the pupils in the eyes
- Muscle contraction
- Release of adrenaline from the adrenal glands
- Conversion of glycogen to glucose to provide more energy for our muscles
- Decrease in saliva production: The stomach doesn't move for digestion, nor does it release digestive secretions
- Decrease in urinary output
- Sphincter contraction

The parasympathetic nervous system can counterbalance the sympathetic nervous system. Its activation restores the body to a calm state of being. Its specific responses are:

- A decrease in heart rate
- Relaxation of muscles
- Reactivation of saliva production: the stomach moves and increases secretions for digestion
- Increase in urinary output
- Sphincter relaxation

As you can see, the frustrations you feel as a result of the bodily reactions (due to sympathetic activation) are not justified since the sympathetic system is doing what it's meant to do. Your emotional and mental state have only joined in on these normal integral reactions. The more we focus on results the more frustrated we become, and the more frustrated we become the longer the sympathetic nervous system will stay activated; the mind-body is producing a self-perpetuating cycle. This chapter is an important eye-opener that I hope will turn you from frustration to understanding while healing health anxiety. The tricky thing though, as briefly mentioned in earlier chapters, is that there are many people that have come to believe that all that comes with sympathetic activation is our normal way of being. We even guzzle more and more caffeinated drinks in order to reach that same point of sympathetic activation because being caffeinated has become our most familiar state of feeling and being. Certain teas do have an effect on activating the parasympathetic system, however, many people will not stick to them consistently since they have been associated with laziness, being unproductive, un-alert, etc. This unconscious reaction and meaning must be internally replaced with a new conscious meaning, as it represents inner peace and a parasympathetic-led system that falls in line with self-empowerment and being content, rather than self-blame and frustration.

The bodily symptoms that are perpetuated by anxiety are normal reactions. If your default state is one of fear, you will continue to be accompanied by the sympathetic-led symptoms mentioned above (and more). Once the feedback loop between mind and body turns from striving and perfection to faith and the pursuit of excellence, the higher self can take over. When the higher self takes over you are no longer living as a mirror of your worry-filled upbringing and you'll get the sense of being 're-born.'

I believe that a body at ease cannot manifest dis-ease.

I believe this because our internal workings are capable of doing their jobs without a fight, without increased effort. To begin the process of turning our default state from being of a sympathetic state to that of a more parasympathetic state we must first have the proper mindset. This includes learning how to adjust to a new way of feeling, to a new way of interacting with the world, and to a new way of living. Let me use the metaphor of two similar cars driving on a highway. One car is moving at top speed while the other at a slower speed. Which car will run down sooner? Which car will need repair for its parts sooner? The one running at top speed, of course. The car that runs at a slower speed also benefits from the chance to be mindful of where it is and of its surroundings. The speedy car, however, can only focus on the path it is on and is more vulnerable to mistakes that could cause an accident. This is similar to how a health anxiety sufferer lives their lives; like a racing car, never mindful of or in real contact with anything other than their immediate internal and external threats. Life is a series of experiences that we turn into safe or threatening memories. When we stay stuck in the interpretations that cause health anxiety, we are creating memories we don't want instead of moving toward the ones that we want to cherish.

Setbacks.

Setbacks for a health anxiety sufferer can come in a host of different forms and I want to bring these to your attention now. It's important to note that these setbacks are only setbacks due to interpreting them as being so. When healing has gained enough momentum these same setbacks become fleeting moments, as we stop internalizing or getting caught up in them anymore. They are:

- Waking up and having that same physical bodily symptom still be there
- Being asked, 'why are you so quiet today' when your full attention is on your bodily symptoms
- Heading to Google for answers
- Asking others in forums and groups if they've felt the same symptoms as you for reassurance purposes
- Crying out of desperation
- Not having the energy or focus to play with your kids

These are just a few experiences we internalize as being setbacks and they only compound our frustrations into further rage directed at ourselves (and often God). Every single one of these 'setbacks' have an unconscious motivation behind them, an important reason led by the inner child to sustain these reactions. These are not consciously led interpretations and actions; they are unconsciously led based on the needs of the inner child to maintain your survival. Your brain has never seen the outside world head-on, but yet now it may deem it as being a dark and scary place based on what your senses and actions have said, hence all the extreme psychological and physiological reactions.

One of the most important lessons I have learned after years of reflection is that my inner child/subconscious mind was most suggestible during the initial moments of spurring on a catastrophic idea, a feeling, or a bodily symptom. During those initial few seconds that I felt something I didn't want to, I began to understand the true power I held to lead my protective parts, rather than be led by what it was that caught my attention (led by sympathetic activation). Remember that for some people this may mean implementing a mental, physiological, verbal, or behavioral skill set, for others it may simply mean inaction. Often, inaction tames the fear since the fear is anticipating a fear reaction, and by not reacting we deny it what it wants. By doing so, we become the observer of fear rather than a partner to it. Just like you can observe a sunset and be in awe of it, so too can you observe an idea or negative feeling and see what its true intentions are: to protect. As we are in the presence of what once led to health anxiety and choose to observe, we are not in a fight between two forces, but rather, we are bringing the two forces, love and fear, together to work in harmony with each other to observe, rather than to react instinctively.

It takes time to become a good observer of anything that normally leads to health anxiety, and this can be frustrating to many. To leave something alone may feel like the very thing that causes you to get worse, and for your catastrophically-led imagination to come true. This is, again, a defense mechanism by the inner child looking to keep you in a familiar place of fear and living instinctually.

When I plant a seed (new direction) and water it often (through certain skill sets or inactions), I don't sit next to the flower to see if it is growing. I leave it alone and let the earth's intelligence take over.

You are planting the seed of new ideas, turning them into beliefs, and letting the results be what they may be, when they may be. There is no frustration when there is trust and certainty. Trust in the fact that you are reading this book and being guided toward healing, and certainty that this health anxiety journey will embed lessons within you that will take you to places of great contribution toward others and the world we live in. This combination of trust and certainty denies any present anger that wants to arise, mainly due to its fear-based roots, and has the potential to pull out all the rage from our bodies connected to our past. Take your time to understand these concepts. Don't rush to the next sentence before truly pulling these new ideas into your heart so that you move toward what you truly deserve, inner peace.

Maladaptive habits lead to more frustration.

If you can identify with any of these habits, understand that they only provide temporary relief. Maladaptive reactions are good at getting rid of symptoms temporarily, but this will lead us to continue to address symptoms but never to address the root causes which lie within memory, identity, secondary gains (the purpose that the symptom serves) and subconscious beliefs.

1) **Eating or drinking disorders** – These are distractions that provide temporary comfort away from the realities of health anxiety. Eating and drinking disorders are also a tell-tale sign of someone whose willpower has been diminished, and therefore looks for the quickest route to some form of inner relief. The important thing here is to begin to associate more pain with this habit consciously, rather than unconsciously associate pleasure with it. The longer a habit has been in place the more challenging it can be (for most people) to create a reversal into a better habit. So for this particular habit, what will the long-term effects be if you continue on this path? Associating pain is a great motivator, as it opens the doorway to seeing the pleasure in a habit that can replace the maladaptive one.

2) **Sensitization** – We all go through a certain level of sensitization prior to unfamiliar upcoming events and this sensitization can be the result of excitement or fear, depending on how we look at it. However, obsessing over how to cope with a situation or how to avoid future events will only lead to constant worrying. This can become a habitual way of living life and is a damaging cycle that we want to refrain from.

3) **Safety activities** – Relying on someone or something to curb or soothe your health anxiety. Consistently carrying a certain item with you as a coping mechanism or needing to physically have

a person around constantly (whether in person or online), for example, can lead to a feeling of powerlessness and frustration. Let me remind you once again that your greatest support person is your own conscious mind. It may take time to master this mind, but it is well worth your efforts.

4) **Avoidance** – Anxious avoidance is to avoid situations that cause anxiety. This only strengthens the threatening associations made in the subconscious mind.

5) **Escape strategy** – I know this habit very well since it is one I employed regularly. I would always sit near the exit doors or bathrooms when out in public. This strategy is often used by people with phobias and panic attacks as they plan and recognize escape routes just in case feelings in the body get out of hand and are no longer controllable. For me, the fear of bringing on attention was just as scary as the symptom itself. Can you relate?

As children we would freeze, helpless in our inability to react in a way that wouldn't allow the subconscious mind to store the experience as a trauma. Now as adults, it's not the bodily symptom that is the problem and the instigator of more fear. But rather, it is our conscious mind's relationship with them that justifies or denies the need for them in the future.

Your thoughts will change, and your feelings and behaviors will too. It's important to couple this with using imagery-based techniques such as image cycling (available through my YouTube channel) to balance out the sympathetic system with the parasympathetic system, just always remember that the body will lag. The physical body is usually the last to catch up to the changes you are making within all the other elements that make up your identity. Naturally, this is where much of our frustrations lie, since while our self-care and emotionally expressive routines may very well be consistent, the body stubbornly stays in a state of fatigue, anxiousness, alertness, and pain. Do not be angered by this, but rather look forward to the next anxious moment as being an opportunity for change.

Life gives us what we want and what we want is communicated by how we feel most often.

When your feeling state changes and becomes your new default way of feeling throughout the day, the internal and external messages your mind and body send will match this frequency. When referring to frequency I'm not speaking about complicated concepts or spiritual woo-woo. Rather, I am referring to an energy force sent through the heart. Your heart is your best friend as must be your own inner child, and you mustn't fear your heart. Feed it the thoughts, words, actions, and inner images that make it sing progress and your praises. This is not selfishness as much as it is necessary self-care, for how can the world be a better place if you are not in a better place yourself? It cannot. Everything is interconnected.

Suffering from health anxiety is frustrating and so is the healing process. You are the one that must choose which type of frustration you want to feel. The one connected to helplessness and inner pain, or the one connected to learning new lessons, experimenting, and building back the trust you lost. You are experimenting and testing new concepts, new meanings, and a new identity. Quite often even positive change can come with a sense of fear. Each day along this healing journey will test your courage to stand up to your old core beliefs, as these core beliefs are connected to your bodily sensations. You must recognize right now which moments of the day demand courage and recognize the willpower that is needed to replace a piece connected to anxiety. I promise, different is not always bad. In this case, different is good. Very good, in fact. You will feel different during moments when you anticipated fear, you will think less in moments where you used to overthink, and you will leave your bodily screams alone when in the past franticness would come upon you.

When healing health anxiety, everything becomes different. Different is good.

Make friends with different, trust me. It will change your life for the better and once something begins feeling different you may look upon it as a sign of progress. This progress is the self-care work you've done in the past that is just now catching up to the present moment. Invite it in and be proud of this very moment that feels different. I remember the years of suffering I went through where a day didn't pass without my inner rage spilling over toward myself and my own father for letting me down as a child. Gradually, I started becoming gentler in all that I thought about myself and all that I did. Therefore, as mentioned, I now refer to my present life as being the 'after life' for myself. A life after a life within the same lifetime. Many don't quite understand this but there are no better words to explain the differences between my first 32 years of my life and the last 10 (I am 42 now as I write this book).

Another noticeable thing during my journey was the inner shift in sensitivity. During health anxiety my mind and body worked together sensitively to protect me from memory fragments connected to past trauma. These days my sensitivity has altered to feel other people's emotional issues even if the words that come out of their mouths don't match what I feel. My empathic abilities have grown and my fear has lessened. I believe many of us who have suppressed our true human capabilities due to health anxiety will find these traits reemerge naturally in great numbers once again as healing progresses into the feeling of being healed. When I mention being healed, I speak of the inability for the irrational fear that used to consume us to no longer do so. In truth, we are always healing in the sense of the spirit. We are setting our spirits free as we once were during childhood, prior to the parental and societal programming we came under. We are all healing something. You are currently healing health anxiety and this is what is necessary to learn what you need to and apply that learning towards your own self-created self-image and self-concept. You are no different than the next person who's working on healing aspects of their own inner world that they aren't satisfied with, so in a sense aren't we always all healing? This should provide you with some cognitive separation away from victimhood and health anxiety. It's something you're doing, not something or someone you are, and you are in the process of doing things differently, which will over time give you a different emotionally-led result.

We were expressive. We loved one another. And we are going back there again through healing health anxiety.

It may be hard for you to imagine this happening in your life right now, but it will become easier in time. Remember, again, that each step within healing demands that you learn the lessons you need to and then consistently and wholeheartedly enact them in your life. Only then will new pieces of wisdom and opportunities present themselves to you.

It's common knowledge that when we are born, we are born with only two fears, all else is learned in this lifetime. These two fears are the fear of falling and the fear of loud noises. However, as is my curious nature, I am not so sure of the idea that we come to this life with only two fears. I believe we carry generational trauma and experiences from past lifetimes with us into this lifetime as well. In my view, you are not just healing your health anxiety, you are emotionally healing future generations within your family tree. For now, though, let's stick to moving beyond our frustrations that we deem as being setbacks.

The easiest thing to be is angered by something unexpected.

What if instead of falling for the anger and allowing it to consume you, you did the opposite. The complete opposite. Practice this and soon it will feel genuine and natural. For now, just considering this idea is enough to pause and assess before beating yourself up with anger again. Consider:

You wake up, feel the bodily sensation, and remind it to stick around for as long as it chooses to. You are no longer consumed by it; you have in a way surrendered to it. Its negative emotional intensity can no longer accommodate the physical symptom.

The formula for this is always the same:

1) Bodily symptom arises
2) Decreased 'what if' thinking (or re-directed 'what if' thinking toward a new optimistic viewpoint)
3) Decreased fearful emotional reaction
4) Symptoms subside over time (often unnoticed until much later)
5) Safety within the environment is projected to the subconscious mind and the inner child now has the green light to feel safe

No frustration, only deeper understanding and cooperation with a system heavily invested in protecting you from the same overwhelming and freezing sensations you once experienced during traumatic instances within your past. These unfamiliar responses to discomfort in mind and body are what the ones who have healed have invested in one day at a time. This is what we now know as being the 'responding' work, which accompanies the 'reframing' work (the dirty work), which eliminates suppressed feelings and personal labels.

The combination of responding and reframing (you can find guided reframing sessions on YouTube or through my online digital programs at www.theanxietyguy.com) is what sets us apart. Responding (or what I like to call 'in the moment work') bypasses the connection that the reptile and emotional brain want to make in order to signify threat. By responding consciously, you begin living consciously, until there comes a time where you can be more unconsciously responsive in all ways once again. So it looks like this:

1) Health anxiety causes unconscious reactions to symptoms or external stimuli based on an idea we have or a feeling we experience.
2) Consciously deciding that we no longer have to be the victim of an idea, of a core belief taken on by our parents, or of a sensation in the body.
3) Taking a stand. Courageously and consistently responding to the bodily screams and catastrophic ideas coming from the inner child in a way where guidance toward the inner child is presented. This can be through one, or a combination of resources, such as mental (replace an old idea with a new one), verbal (expression of feelings and ideas rather than suppression), behavioral (acting in

opposition to fear), physiological (slowing down, breathing more deeply, straightening posture), or imagery (imagining a better or different outcome).

4) Taking a stand can also mean complete inaction, to leave whatever just arose alone. Inaction is still a form of action, but it demands a deep level of trust and faith in order to do so with a sense of certainty. For instance, after years of reframing and responding work, I no longer feel the need to enact a skill set when a fear might randomly arise. Rather, I have so much evidence behind me and trust that it will all be fine should I just leave it alone, that I do. When you no longer fall for the lies your mind or body tell you, you can move away from health anxiety and be a proud, certain, and unlimited soul once again.

5) Becoming. A place where you connect deeply with a new identity and core belief system. I will go deeper into this portion of the health anxiety healing journey in later chapters. But in brief, this is the afterlife I discuss within this lifetime.

Life is simply a series of experiences, and we must choose who we truly want to be from one experience to the next.

Yes, it is a choice. Often, though, health anxiety sufferers aren't very confident in the choices they make themselves out of a low level of self-worth and an over-reliance on others. This is nothing to fret over, nothing to feel guilty about. Rather, it is a chance to bring focus to what has been missing in our lives up until now. Emotional maturity is to act not out of feeling, but out of a newfound approach to life. Be proud of yourself. You are here, you are reading this book, and you are healing. Soon your own inner child will get on board with your new conscious beliefs and safety and self-love will overwhelm any fears that want to show up in the future. Just keep learning, just keep applying, just keep going.

Chapter 7:
Victimhood: The 'Why Me' Cycle

At some point along this journey—quite often just before a great breakthrough in fact—victimhood will strike. You will look around and notice everyone enjoying their days seemingly at great peace with themselves while you wonder why you must go through what you are going through. This experience will be in the background throughout most of your health anxiety days, and will erupt into your awareness during moments when you truly want to be present and enjoying yourself, at a time when all you can focus on is your bodily symptoms of anxiety or another component around health anxiety. You try your best to be present, but you find yourself imagining a spiraling and potentially catastrophic future based on the associations created by your past once again. You soon feel a tremendous weight around guilt flooding your mind, body, and spirit. You curse your parents, your job, your neighborhood, your friends, even your interpretation of God, as the emotional intensity of that very moment heightens. The opportunity to make long-lasting and cherished memories passes while your gratitude for surviving your suffering heightens. Life becomes a fight for survival with every uncomfortable bodily feeling, every piece of catastrophic news from the outside, and every panic attack. You seem to latch onto anything that maintains your suffering while simultaneously wishing it all be taken away in one swift moment. Soon you may find yourself relying solely on quick fixes. This is a creative trick by the inner child which keeps you suffering for longer and prevents you from committing to the long-term reframing and responding work necessary for true progress and health anxiety healing.

This pattern continues in this fashion until the moment we recognize that what we think we need to do for ourselves only keeps us confined to a place of familiar suffering, a familiar identity. This is a vital moment that must be grasped fully and reflected upon. Since it is this deeper reflection that will bring to your attention the things that have been outside of your awareness for far too long. Once we can see beyond these patterns, we realize how much money, time, and energy has been wasted on what we thought were solutions that at best only helped to subside our symptoms temporarily.

Victimhood is a state of being that too many of us get too comfortable in.

The reason for this is that victimhood is motivated by the inner child. This proves that we are, or will be, receiving something we couldn't when we weren't victims. These include but aren't limited to: attention from our partners, bodily contact, financial help, and concern from others. We even justify not taking risks in our lives because we have an excuse. Health anxiety in general can be a very good reason for us to stave off responsibility for people, new career choices, or anything else we look to avoid out of fear. The inner child may even create mental confusion during moments when we want to show our empowerment and transition to the world, which leads to the wrong words or actions coming out, and, in turn, this takes us right back into familiar victimhood. Your inner child doesn't believe victimhood is a bad thing—it believes it's a good thing and will do everything in its power to get you to not change. Backward thinking, I know. But remember, it's what your subconscious deems as being safest for you.

Also, we may unconsciously take on victimhood from our fathers and mothers.

As young children, our parents were our gods. Whatever they thought, said, and did created the blueprint for what was right and wrong within our minds. They were our main guides and as children, we learn more from what we see than from what we hear. So, when a father wakes up in the morning and complains of aches and pains or a mother reminds the family of how incapable she is in her work, we feel for them and we model after them. There are many instances of this modeling behavior taking place in your life right now. You must reflect on this (not over-analyze) and be honest with yourself in order to begin breaking away. You cannot both overcome health anxiety and stay as a victim at the same time. You must choose between the secondary gains you may be receiving from playing the victim and the uncertainty of this new healing journey. You honestly must choose, and your actions must match your decision. It's easy to say this and more challenging to implement. However, if you choose to stay the victim, how much longer will you be using this excuse for? Yes, anything new you attempt will be challenging at first, but it will be rewarding in the end. If you've made the decision to step out of victimhood starting today, today will be the worst you'll ever be at your new identity and the persona parts that accompany it. Remember that this recognition will bring on a gentler dialogue between you and your inner child the next time you feel you've somehow 'failed' or had a setback. Your health anxiety healing is determined by how you deal with challenging times, and not by those moments throughout the day when emotional neutrality is present and nothing much is taking place internal or external in terms of challenges.

This is where you begin tapping back into the true power within, the power you thought you lost for good.

In my personal experiences with victimhood, I remember how it led to parking myself on my couch and watching every movie available. Depressing, yes, but it also allowed me time away from my co-workers, my boss, and my clients, which meant that I was internally fighting less. It wasn't a very fulfilling time in my life, but at the same time I did feel some sort of relief within this victimhood identity. Friends and family checked in on me regularly, that was nice. However, I realized that I was pinpointing the idea that it was the people and situations that perpetuated my anxiety, when this wasn't true at all. My fears around self-expression were at the root of it all and my thoughts at the time were that no one would consider a friendship with me should my true colors shine through. I was running one unconsciously led and self-defeating movie after movie in my mind. None of these movies had any truth to them, but they did occupy my mind enough to keep my body sensitized further. Little do others realize that a health anxiety sufferer wants nothing more than normalcy in their lives, that's it. If you ask them what their goals are they wouldn't even be able to fathom a different career, relationships, or living on a tropical island one day. They just want to feel normal again. They want to move out of their heads and into their hearts, they want to stop allowing their bodies to consume all their focus, and they want people around them that will listen, but at the same time help them to challenge their greatest fears. They don't want to be victims of their present circumstances, they want to see the light, feel the light. However, we must consider the fact that if we do not truly believe in something new consciously, the subconscious mind will create its own meaning and belief, therefore creating an action for us. Choose a path or one will be chosen for you.

Everything on this planet that we experience through our 5 senses has a meaning to it. That meaning can either perpetuate a state of anxiety or create a feeling of emotional neutrality. We must understand this and begin captaining our own ships. When referring to 'captaining our own ships' many of us already intuitively know how to do this. As in which past experiences need reframing, which relationships need fixing (which often means verbally expressing what we couldn't at the time), and which 'responses' we must implement in moments of fear and anxiousness. Never allow the inner child to convince you that you have no clue on how to deal with your inner or outer challenges. This is again a creative defense mechanism to keep things the same.

We are much more intelligent and intuitive than we think.

It may make you feel uncomfortable knowing this, however, healing health anxiety and general anxiety doesn't happen until we recognize and begin stepping out of our comfort zones. The more dissatisfied a person becomes and the closer they are to rock bottom, the more direct they will be in their actions to step out of their comfort zones. The ones that haven't gotten to what I like to call 'the point of no return' may find a more progressive and systematic approach to be to their liking. Neither is wrong. However, having said that, when I work with people personally or in a workshop environment, I like to hit their pain button often. Getting them to this point where healing health anxiety is a must, and not a should, makes the journey forward a little more linear. We question ourselves less and we truly put our heart into our inner work. The opposite of this would be the approach of 'faking it until we make it', which rarely works in my experience. Practicing it until you master it would be a much better mindset going forward out of victimhood, since isn't every anxious moment a practice opportunity anyway? What exactly are we practicing, though? We're practicing allowing certain thoughts and persona parts that have been suppressed to come out and join our actions in the very moments when we defy our old unconscious reactions.

Making the connection.

There is one aspect of your life that you are proud of. You're so proud of it, in fact, that you struggled with it at some point. You played the victim along this journey at one point as well, but overcame it, maybe even swiftly. Can you pinpoint which aspect this is now? Could it be connected to your:

- Current career or business that you built?
- Relationship with your husband or wife?
- Learning a new language?
- Times when studying an important course?
- Moments when you were learning how to drive?
- Understanding how to be a good father or mother?
- Experiences when you helped a friend out of a troubling situation?

Think of this experience now. When you've found it, did you notice what you did to move yourself out of victimhood and out of the difficult situation as a whole? What sort of steps did you take? What sort of realizations did you meet along the journey? Understand this: if you could overcome victimhood and that past challenge, you can overcome victimhood now during this health anxiety challenge and end the suffering you are experiencing recently as well. Tap into the formula you used and move that person into the person you are today. What hesitations do you have when looking to do this? If there's one thing

I can be sure of with health anxiety healing, it's that the right mindset will provide many intelligent and intuitive answers when we need them most. During the times when you overcame your old helplessness and victimhood you had the right mindset. What was it?

As you reflect on these ideas I want to present you with another imagery-focused skill set that you can use alongside mapping and image cycling. Read the instructions fully before implementing this technique in an environment where you won't be bothered for a few minutes:

Close your eyes and imagine two separate pictures, one to your left and to your right. The picture on the left represents a time in your life when you overcame your fears, when you left a place of suffering, even possibly victimhood, and felt empowered. The picture on the right represents a recent experience of health anxiety for you. Maybe it was upon waking up in the morning, driving, or any other time you were struggling. Now count from 3 down to 1, and as you do you will move the person on the left into the person on the right (make a woosh sound as you make the transition), and simply observe what is taking place. Consider the new person you have made. What happens in that same situation now? How do you respond to symptoms, your thoughts, outside information, anything that activated health anxiety within you? As you observe what it's like for the empowered person to experience those same old 'triggers' that once moved you into health anxiety, how does it feel now? The 'total transition' technique is one that when used consistently will empower you to make different choices in moments of fear.

I would recommend that out of all the imagery-based techniques you learn in this book for health anxiety, you only use one per day. Do not think that more is better, as more often than not doing more will just give you the opposite result of what you desire. Instead, do a few total transition processes upon waking up in the morning and take note of what internal changes you encounter throughout the day. Remember, the goal is to become bored and disinterested in those things we used to call 'triggers' to our health anxiety. When boredom arises, we can see them as fleeting experiences rather than ones we must pay further attention to. I personally love this technique because it opens the mind to what is possible for us during challenging moments.

In Neuro-Linguistic Programming—a modeling method to bring about our goals and desires that I use from time to time in my teachings—there is a saying that goes 'you already have everything you need within you'. For the most part, I do believe this to be true, especially when we begin doing our own thinking and stop being led by the messages we get online and from society. I do believe that staying in the 'why me' cycle is a choice, to a large extent. Does that mean we must berate ourselves for being in this state? Absolutely not. I am simply showing you what's available to you and what's possible for you. One of the greatest lessons I learned on my own healing journey was that if you continue to give a sufferer what they expect to hear, see, or feel, they will stay stuck. If, however, the sufferer is challenged to question their old ways and experiences the right kind of discomfort when a supporter looks to help, it can spur on a change in belief systems. For example, when I was at the peak of my health anxiety days, I asked my fiancée at the time Robyn to punch me in the shoulder whenever I started to play the victim or when I just looked like I was too obsessively in my head. This was one of a few methods we used as a 'state break' to snap me out of my familiar but self-sabotaging ways. Since Robyn and I spent so much time together at the beginning of our relationship (still do in fact) she was my 'go-to' person whenever I needed support. But at the time my idea of support was someone who would tell me that I wasn't going to die or that my symptoms weren't the path to illness. However, even when I received this confirmation from Robyn (as well as numerous physicians and family members), it only helped me temporarily. This is why it is very important that your main support person—the person you spend the most time with—doesn't keep feeding into what you want from them, since most of the time what you want from them is reassurance and this only keeps the cycle of suffering alive. Instead, ask them to tell you a dirty joke, tell them to remind you to take a 15-second cold shower, or even to ask you silly questions like 'why is the moon made out of green cheese'. In those very moments, victimhood looks to come to the surface.

I find that the best state breaks are achieved through a physical act, as a physiological jolt will help to get you thinking again and not replaying old ideas.

Let's also consider the opposite type of health anxiety sufferer, the one that likes to 'keep everything in' and never share any information in regards to their suffering. These people don't like to get in the way of other people's lives and feel like if they do, they'll pay the price with an even greater sense of self-blame and guilt. The negative emotional weight is already heavy for these people and the idea of even more added on seems disastrous. If suppression is pain then expression is healing, always remember that. When we express, however, we must always consider the fact that our inner children are always listening, always noting, and always translating into meaning and belief what comes out of our mouths. If we say the words 'why does this always happen to me' the inner child will respond with 'oh, I guess they want a list made up!'. This only creates further victimhood and suffering, so this kind of thinking and expression is not beneficial long term. Neither is the fake kind where we say, 'I feel great today thanks for asking!' The inner child knows you're lying because the words don't match the feelings, which means that the conscious thought does not match the subconscious one. Pretend positivity only justifies the emotional suppression we've been under all these years and creates a different form of suffering that I like to refer to as toxic positivity. This is not a genuine place led by the higher self, but rather a place where we fall victim to words we've touched on earlier such as 'trying' (which implies an inability to complete something), 'hoping' (which has determined that there's little to no chance of the change actually happening), and 'but' (where we mention our progress prior to mentioning a part that was still imperfect, which in turn negates the progress as well).

Starting today, don't allow yourself to solely speak of your flaws and suffering. Don't suppress everything that arises within your thoughts and feelings, both mentally or physically. Instead, speak about the new insights you've gained and developed. Speak about your progress in a way where you truly are beginning to replace fear with faith along a healing journey that is beautifully uncertain.

Interestingly, most health anxiety sufferers who've followed and applied my content for some time are making much more progress than they are experiencing setbacks. But often their thoughts, words, and actions don't speak this truth. Thoughts are energy, words are energy, action is energy, running images in your head is energy. It all takes up energy, which means we must begin consciously using our energy in ways that keep us moving in the direction of our own truths, not the truths of our authority figures, no matter how much we love them. None of us are going to live forever so we must stop putting off our healing steps starting today.

It all starts with honesty; you must look into the mirror and be brutally honest with yourself in terms of what is really keeping you stuck. Not the things or the people in your environment, I'm talking about the blocks that were laid down based on personal experiences. Who are you really angry with, still? When did you really lose your sense of self-worth? Which experience speaks to you initially? These are the kinds of questions we ask and allow our intuition to answer, no matter how silly or far fetched the answer may seem to our conscious minds. This is the healing path and it is called depth. We mustn't be afraid of going deep, since healing truly will manifest for you when you begin to acknowledge what you've suppressed for far too long and start doing something about it with all your heart.

Chapter 8:
Choosing To Let Go of Control

Distraction is not a strategy for healing health anxiety, but it may be one you unconsciously revert to whenever something uncomfortable arises. In today's world, it seems impossible not to use distraction as a strategy when we feel challenged, because our response to distraction makes us feel like the solution lies within it. Many health anxiety sufferers feel that if they can just distract themselves repeatedly, that at some point their bodies will stop screaming out with symptoms, or their minds will stop the endless catastrophic chatter. It's a strategy seeped within hope—and hope is certainly a great place to start a healing journey—but an awful long-term strategy to assume consistently.

Do you…

1) Look for reassurance from an online support group or forum when physical sensations appear?

2) Turn to your phone when you're sitting at a café and someone you absolutely can't stand walks in?

3) Play with a gadget of some sort whenever you feel stress arising?

4) Turn the music up in your car louder every time an old disheartening memory pops into your head?

5) Turn to processed foods each time you want to make yourself feel better after what seems like an awful day?

These are just a few examples of distraction action. What if, however, we considered a different response rather than an instinctual 'reaction' in these exact moments? What would we feel and what would happen then? Let's take a look at scenario #1...

- A physical sensation appears. You realize how you've been sitting for hours, which has led to the constriction you feel in your body and your breathing pattern. In that very moment, you remind yourself to go for a walk to allow the sensations and screams of your inner child to subside whenever and however they may while your breathing deepens and your focus gently and slowly turns to your naturalistic environment.

This would be the definition of responding rather than replaying. Often health anxiety sufferers feel something and allow their thoughts and actions to play along with that initial feeling. However, once we can truly understand that the feeling is involuntary and we didn't create it based on whatever may be taking place on the outside, we can begin to understand that we have two main parts to us, unconscious and conscious. As the conscious parts of us grow stronger and lead the way, the unconscious parts subside and take a back seat to the meanings we place on things and what we do. This is how we take power back from our unconscious parts; this is how we bring back peace to our inner world again. Let's look at scenario #2...

- While sitting at the café a person you're not very fond of walks in, and instead of distracting yourself or hiding away somehow, you realize that this is just another test from the universe to see whether you believe in the new ideas you want to make true for you. Another conscious response, and a good one, since the universe will constantly find new ways to test us in our path to inner healing. As we recognize that this is one of those challenging moments, we continue sipping our tea and reading our books, ignoring whether that other person notices us or not. We are no longer focused on the outcome or feel a need to control the situation and have the result be what our inner child's want it to be. We are free from all of that, we are present, and we are putting ourselves first once again.

Generalized anxiety often leads to health anxiety, so the confidence built around overcoming general anxiety will trickle down and build trust in the body's own ability to deal with sensations and symptoms once again.

Many health anxiety sufferers think that their obsessiveness with their health is the main problem, when in reality it is their obsessiveness to maintain that sense of certainty and control over their lives.

Life becomes much too complicated when any form of anxiety leads the day. We unconsciously begin placing tremendous value on analyzing every single symptom and external moment because we are so afraid of the uncertainty that may arise if we don't. This kind of rigid approach to life blocks us from manifesting our true desires, both for ourselves and our families, since the universe picks up on our core desires to always keep things as they are. There is no space here for wonder, creativity, or play. The very idea of dancing to a beautiful drum beat, for example, makes us cringe when in reality this is another way of letting go. It's the letting go part that is one of the most challenging aspects of healing. Letting go of the way the inner child wants things to be and guiding that inner voice back to what is true. What is true is very much connected to how we saw life at the earliest years of our experience in this lifetime. We must go backward in many ways to go forward again, and watching children play may be the best kind of learning a health anxiety sufferer can provide to themselves these days. On to scenario #3...

- Instead of playing with a gadget each time you feel a sense of overwhelm and stress come over you, your response is a self-hug instead. Deep down we crave connection and touch, but little do we realize that these things will never manifest to the level we deserve with anyone else until we reach the level we deserve with our own inner child. A self-hug in moments of stress provides comfort, and connectedness, and is free and available anytime. In life we unconsciously go out of our way and do some crazy things in the hopes of feeling connected, accepted, and loved by others. However, we always seem to be left wanting, never truly satisfied with the results. Self-hugs, however, will always lead to the feeling you deserve and need to feel daily. Your inner child deserves to be treated better than how you have been treating them lately anyway, so from now on stress leads to self-hugs. Just make sure you don't go looking for stress just because you look so forward to these self-hugs.

These are responding skill sets that you may not have been open to up until now. However, when life picks up too much speed, when we put everything and everyone before the re-building of the relationship with our bodies and spirits, we begin leading random lives rather than fulfilling ones. When life picks up too much speed, we look to what can offend us further within our immediate environment rather than what we are grateful for now. This is living in survival. In healing health anxiety, there will come a time to reflect, a time to think, a time to act, a time to imagine something new, a time to speak up, etc. We recognize when these times arise by the fading of inner chatter and as we stop looking to protect ourselves from each potential threat that life may throw at us. As our intuitiveness grows our mental chatter subsides and when this happens even the fear of death is replaced with surrendering to the uncertainties around it. Scenario #4...

- You're driving in your car and suddenly a feeling of rage comes over you connected to the time dad could have shown his love to you within a particular childhood moment. Instead of turning the music up louder and suppressing the feelings deep into parts of our bodies, why not express your anger instead? We live in a society where we are taught that it's wrong to express how we feel. We label our issues as 'mental health' disorders rather than understanding deeply that we are dealing with suppressed feelings and emotions that manifest as mental health and physical challenges. In that very moment of rage, pull your car over, put it in park, and express your dissatisfaction with your dad as if he was sitting in the passenger seat beside you. This rageful moment presents an opportunity to unload much of the emotional baggage we carry around in our bodies. Our voices are the tools we can use to carry us away from a traumatic past and toward a consciously created future. Your body will tremble as you speak up, it will sweat, and you will cry. These are all part of the 'purging' process that leads to healing of all sorts. This is the 'messy work' that I refer to often in my speaking engagements that we are afraid to do out of fear of revealing. To reveal is to heal.

Many times after such deeply felt expression, of tackling the roots of our fears, we become tired. Physically and energetically. We feel lighter, and tired, and this is good. I can't tell you how many times after a traumatic reframing process with a client that I could see the surrender in them, the lightness in them. Sometimes it literally takes sickness or illness to reveal to a person what needs emotional expression. These moments are opportunities to wake up and step out of what I call 'robotic consciousness.' This is a survival trance state led by our survival mechanisms. When there is verbal expression there is also physiological expression. We chip away at the old trance state and begin feeling things we haven't felt for a long time, like self-love and worthiness, for instance. Often this scares a person back into their old trance state, though, since they feel undeserving of such positive feelings toward themselves. Their perfectionistic parts show up and say, 'well you never accomplished what you set out to accomplish yet, which shows you don't deserve the self-love you're feeling right now'. Trust me, there are a lot of perfectionists in the health anxiety world, so if you are one of them you are far from being alone. Perfectionism is nothing more than a dire need for control and certainty.

Can you live with the idea that your health doesn't have to be perfect in order for you to feel good about yourself and your life?

It's an important question to answer. Too often we need everything to be ideal in order for us to feel satisfied. A health anxiety sufferer, for instance, can have 3 quarters of their day be without symptoms, peaceful and gentle, and in the evening have one heart palpitation that sets the tone for the next few weeks, even. Until, that is, we connect the heart palpitation to the horror or action movie we are supposed to go to that evening, only with this kind of conscious response can we keep our positive momentum going.

Verbal expression doesn't mean you have to be reckless, though. It just means you have to pick your opportunities well. Chair coaching for instance (look up 'chair coaching the anxiety guy' on YouTube for a deep explanation of this technique) is a pre-planned face-to-face imaginative visit (which tends to feel more real than we ever thought initially) with someone from your past. Through chair coaching, you get to speak up directly to the person that has something to do with your anxieties today. Maybe it's your mother that you need to speak to in order to let her know that you love her dearly, but can no longer carry the burden of being anxious as she once was. Or maybe the person sitting across from you is your old sports coach who demanded too much of you and never allowed you to be satisfied with your past achievements. Expression reveals to us the truth behind our belief systems. The truth revealed is that so much of who we've become today is nothing more than a mirror image of others.

We come to this world unique and often we leave it as a replica of someone else.

This doesn't have to be you. Health anxiety healing is providing you with the opportunities to find inner peace and self-love once again. Finally, let's check in with scenario #5...

- You've had a challenging day, you come home, and your internal gas tank is empty. You're out of 'willpower points' due to all the fighting you did to maintain consistency and control in your life, and you're thinking of what the fastest way to feeling better is. Your inner child decides that pizza and fries would be the most satisfying, however, your conscious mind sees that this has become a pattern in your life. When this is the case, we often unconsciously look to have bad days and maintain our anxiety because of the processed food reward that we will meet with at the end of the day. It gives us a reason to stay in survival mode, to drain our gas tank, so to speak. This leads to a perpetual state of fear and victimhood. The conscious mind sees this pattern in that very moment and decides to give the body what it really needs instead; rest, along with a mix of healthy fats, a good source of protein, and vegetables. The immediate and elevated feelings of satisfaction that junk food provides may not be there. However, at an intuitive level, you feel you've made the right choice for your long-term health. This is not easily done, as junk food can be just as difficult, if not more so, to replace than certain street drugs, even. These addictive patterns are all interconnected and woven together through our eating and entertainment habits. When you are in the healing process you are no longer dragged around by advertisements, junk food, favorite sports teams, the competitive rat race in the workplace, video games, action-packed movies, or other ways. When we find inner peace, what once felt boring and unsatisfying to us feels blissful once again, such as a walk in the park, a physical book, or an open and respectful conversation with someone. At this point, the over-stimulation has ended and is replaced with calm. We see, hear, feel, taste, and smell things clearly here.

When our bodies find homeostasis, our minds tap into the power of neuroplasticity, and our spirits are set free to believe in whatever god we deem to fit us perfectly in this chapter in our lives.

When you leave your old self-sabotaging and distracting habits, be prepared for plenty of confusion and even belittlement from others. People around you won't like the change, since they got along so well with the person you have been for so long now (even if it meant emotionally ill health). Don't allow the words and energies of those around you to make you question your path forward and away from health anxiety (and anxiety in general). Spending less time in a toxic environment only opens more time to spend in a cleansing environment. Even the music you start to listen to may change, as it has for me. During my years of health anxiety and in the trance state of robotic consciousness I would turn the radio on in my car and listen to whatever played on what I thought was my 'favorite' station. It wasn't my favorite station really, it was what I saw and heard most often in my life and what I defaulted to while driving, that's all. I remember an epiphany that I spontaneously ran into one day during my battles with multiple anxiety disorders while driving and listening to a song called 'Work' by the singer Rihanna. The word 'work' was said a staggering 75 times in a matter of a few minutes! Combine that with a song beat that can be catchy and a specific tone that we latch onto, and you have subliminal and subconscious programming at its finest. I remember thinking in that very moment that the songs I was listening to, the food I was eating, the TV I was watching, the drinks I was having, and the malls I was shopping in didn't have my best interest at heart. Quite the opposite, in fact, since emotional or physical sickness have become so very profitable in today's chaotic world. I know I may sound a little extreme here, but my only wish is to bring to your conscious awareness the things that may be perpetuating your anxiety that you are unaware of and deem as being normal everyday things.

Soon after that epiphany, I ran into an artist named Ajeet. She had the voice of an angel and challenged me to go deeper into bringing true meaning to my own life and heal my anxiety for good.

Her songs provided me with deeper clarity, and I highly recommend you give her a listen when you have time. The messages are so very healing and uplifting and will only support you in what you are trying to accomplish here with healing health anxiety. In turn, we must understand that when we bring our attention to the fact that we have more options than we originally thought in regard to our daily habits, we then have choices to make. We can choose to stay where we are, or we can choose to completely change where we are. As your level of certainty increases toward a simpler life of creation rather than a stimulated life of survival, even the old taste of coffee you once relied on each morning begins to taste rotten. Herbal teas begin supporting your path as a replacement and you begin to wonder what changes you will come across next. Change begins to have a nice ring to it and the fear of uncertainty turns into the embrace of uncertainty. The fear of illness is replaced with a trust in healing, and the avoidance of bodily sensations is replaced with the welcoming of the body's messages. Healing doesn't mean endless happiness as much as it means being in a heightened state of trust and faith. Happiness is the marketing messages we hear daily; trust and faith-based messages we must do a little more digging for and be open to. My hope is that you see the opportunity in front of you. To you, it may seem like just overcoming the fear of bodily sensations and potential disease, but there is much more at play here. Healing health anxiety is more than mindfulness. It is healing the soul, reprogramming the subconscious mind, and re-directing our life's path to show us purpose. Keep going, keep learning, keep applying, and soon you will become more than your health anxiety, I promise.

Chapter 9:
The Fear of Passing Health Anxiety onto Our Children

A helicopter parent is a person that wants to be involved in and lead every aspect of their child's life. My advice to you? Work on not being one of these types of parents. More often than not we unknowingly pass on our insecurities and belief systems to our kids, and the last thing we truly want is for them to have to go through life with negative experiences that they don't necessarily have to experience. There was a time in my life when I thought, felt, and pictured ill health in my own child. As I look back, I can't believe how real the threat looked at the time, when in reality it was simply a story I was making up. Thoughts, pictures, and feelings are energy and I unknowingly passed on my fears to my child. At the early stages of his life, I didn't allow my child to see the world through his own perceptions but rather shared my own insecurities daily around how threatening this world really was.

It's one thing to be aware of a child's health, it's another thing to be obsessed over it.

We approach the raising of our children with the best intentions, we really do. However, the problem lies in our instinctive decision-making when it comes to their growth rather than our intelligent or intuitive decision-making.

Meaning, we as anxious parents often find ourselves in a limbo between over-protecting our children and letting life teach them what they need. This over-protectiveness is a reflection of our own fears and distrusts that we pour into our children many times unknowingly. We deem ourselves as being 'bad mothers or fathers' if we pass on an opportunity to guide them in some direction that we believe may benefit them. Again, the best intentions, but often highly unnecessary. Health anxiety is our 'big challenge' when it comes to learning major life lessons that will propel us toward living in a whole new conscious dimension in mind, body, and spirit, though it most likely isn't your own child's. They will have their own fears and challenges that they'll need to work through, and we want to make sure that during their childhood we give them as few 'traumatic' experiences as possible to save them from having to clean them up later on in their lives. Let me remind you once again that a traumatic event is dependent on the perception, not the experience itself. This is important since health anxiety sufferers must understand that what feels normal to them in terms of fear will not feel normal to others, especially to their own children. What we think are real threats will look like flies buzzing around our faces in the future. This is good. It shows that we have come a long way in upgrading our core beliefs and aligning them with our conscious beliefs.

When it comes to children, we must understand that the early years between conception and the age of 5 is where the vast majority of their understandings and beliefs will form. These are those crucial years when we, as parents, are responsible for showing them that an open-minded and open-hearted approach to life is key. They may not have their critical thinking faculties up and running yet, however, the kind of thinking that they do start doing only a few years later will depend on their life experiences between conception and the age of 5. Keep this in mind as well; just because you emotionally and energetically feel like you may have passed on some of your health anxiety to them during these years doesn't mean it cannot be reversed. As they go from one default brainwave state to another during childhood and their teen years, they are still forming core beliefs. For example, during the alpha brainwave state (creativity and wonder) they find themselves in around the age of 7, they are very much in 'play mode'. These are important years where the body can become the mind, where safety can be projected in all environments during play. I truly believe that the sooner a child, adolescent, or teen begins connecting their emotions to their inner child's emotions, the better. It's important for the child to understand that an initial feeling isn't final in their decision-making and behaviors. An emotional response to anything is simply one perception, one idea, and they must learn to consider other ones as well. Along these lines are 5 points I would like you to consider as a current or future parent who is on the path to healing their own health anxiety. These points will guide you toward helping your child/children become their unique and best versions of themselves.

1. One person's tragic story doesn't have to be your own.

This one point changed my entire approach to parenting, truly. Years ago, during the beginning of my own health anxiety healing journey, I realized that there was one story that stuck to me right at my core. That story was about how a toddler tragically drowned in a backyard pool while the parents were busy with other things. This story activated my sympathetic system and turned me into a 'helicopter parent' early on. This tragedy affected every area of my own parenting and I unconsciously wanted to make sure a certain level of threat perception was assumed by my own child no matter what he did.

I remember constantly using the words 'be careful' until I replaced it with 'be aware'.

This may or may not have to do with health anxiety itself, but all anxieties connect to some degree. To 'be careful' is to see the experience from the perspective that it is dangerous, to 'be aware' is to balance out safety and threat and give the child the green light to build their decisions and beliefs about the experience themselves. These types of words and approaches allow our own fight or flight and rest and digest systems to be in balance which, in turn, will allow our decision-making and guidance to be open and nurturing rather than closed off and potentially destructive.

No matter what child-related tragedy lives in your unconscious or conscious mind that is negatively affecting your parenting (and ultimately your relationship with your child), understand that one person's experience doesn't have to lead to yours. You don't have to see the world through the eyes of a tragedy-stricken parent anymore. You can leave that world behind starting right now. That doesn't mean we're being less compassionate by any means; it just means that we have made a decision not to carry the weight that others may be carrying. The life lessons and epiphanies we come across as living human beings are very similar. However, we attain them in different ways and through different experiences. In the end, the universe looks to lead us in the direction of living life within the laws of nature, which is opposite to how the media and societal conditioning want us to live our lives. Put the heavy weight down today. It's their story, not yours. It's their way of meeting with the lessons we all have a chance to meet with, not ours.

2. Be reminded of other possibilities and work on attaching feelings to them.

The possibilities in terms of what something means are endless, the question is: which possibility best fits with the person you are trying to create within you? Since instincts are led by the tag team actions of our survival and emotional brains, this leaves little room for exploration into other perceptions and meanings. However, when we can start seeing ourselves from a new point of view, we become open to perceptions that fit in line with that new identity. In terms of connecting this to the health anxiety you experience because of analyzing your own children's health, you can remind yourself that:

- Children's bodies are very resilient
- What you think is a threat to their lives is most likely something very minor
- Never allow your anxiety to decide what the health of your own child looks like

Of course, there are a million and one other possibilities. Your job is not to tap into all of them in regards to your child's good health, it is to connect to one and only one that fits with factual thinking. The facts will highly favor good health and a long and healthy life for your child. Just remember that factual thinking must be met with a feeling that it is true, or else your heart won't accompany the thought into a new belief system. One idea coupled with enough added feeling has the potential to turn the old catastrophic thought into a fresh new one. If I were you, I would take each idea that comes from the subconscious mind (that we now know as the inner child) with a grain of salt. Meaning, question it. Your child has come to this world for a purpose that only he or she will understand later in life, once lessons are taken from the other trials and tribulations he or she goes through in this lifetime. Once we can begin thinking in this manner, we will be brought to a place of leaving a catastrophic idea alone, and this is the true end goal.

3. Run mental movies of your healthy children each morning and evening before sleeping.

The power of running mental slideshows in our minds of the present or future we desire is extremely powerful, as tapped into earlier in this book. If health anxiety in regards to your children is eating away at your own life experience, take a few moments upon waking up and just before going to sleep to imagine your child or children experiencing life with vibrant health. See the beautiful white aura glowing around them as they play in their favorite playground with a massive smile on their faces. Remember, you can run these slideshows in any environment with anyone at any time, so get very specific in terms of when exactly the fear of them developing some kind of illness comes over you. The pictures that you run with a deep sense of certainty attached to them will determine your future. Sometimes these mental movies manifest into physical reality and other times in slightly different ways. Either way, you are planting seeds. No longer will we plant seeds of doubt when it comes to our children's health, since this is what we've been unconsciously doing for some time now. Instead, we will plant seeds of trust. Trust in life to provide the kind of optimal mind, body, and spirit health that these children deserve.

Have fun with your mental movies. Too often we try to make them perfect and give up too soon. Instead, play with these pictures more. Playfulness is a necessary component for change to work and releases a high level of the hormone known as oxytocin, which increases our brain's ability to tap into neuroplasticity (re-wiring the brain). Simply said, it's easier to create core belief changes when there is a sense of playfulness that accompanies your mental movie sessions. Soon you'll be enjoying this process so much that not running your mental movies may make you feel like a very valuable habit in your life is missing. This is good.

4. Understand the great price you are paying for maintaining this worry habit.

When we bring something unconscious to our conscious mind's attention, we have the chance to change it into whatever we want it to mean or be. You are currently paying a very high price for allowing catastrophic ideas around your child's health to dictate both your actions and theirs. Life cannot be lived with an open mind and an open heart when we are closed off to other potentials. Therefore, it's vitally important that you bring to your attention some of the things you may be missing out on if you continue to allow these patterns to run your life. Such as:

- Tapping into your own childhood wonder and creativity
- Valuable play time with your kids
- Allowing your kids to have adventurous experiences that will turn into lifelong memories

These are just a few reasons why it's vital that your worry habit be ceased starting today. Key words: starting today. As they say, Rome wasn't built in a day. However, just as a sculptor chips away at his or her sculpture, so are you chipping away at your health anxiety. The speed at which you see these changes is not important. What is important is that you sense that progress is being made even though your inner child will make you think it isn't.

5. Every example you give of 'letting go' shows your own children that this world is safe.

Their brains and bodies will not feel like they must go out of their way to protect themselves at every instance. A weight will be lifted from their shoulders once we can associate enough pain with not changing and enough pleasure with changing. These are the two motivational paths and when we use them both in our change work, the magic starts to appear. Let's be honest, wouldn't it be better in all aspects to be the 'cool mom' or 'cool dad' anyway?

6. Allow your children to teach you, even more so than you teach them.

A child is born to teach us how to tap back into our creative and wondrous selves again, and to show us how we've wavered in terms of the meanings we've placed on life. Each day is a new opportunity to be taught, rather than feel like we need to teach them so much. You're not a better parent because your every word or action dictates how they think and what they do, you're a better parent because balance is once again felt on the inside in terms of your approach to life and parenting. Conscious parenting is wonderful, and it makes us look at how we parented in the past and shake our heads. Things that once had dire importance don't matter anymore and our priorities begin to take good shape once again. The inner child prefers to teach and show first, and be taught and shown second. It is most definitely open to changes in meaning and beliefs, however, it needs a history of success before the changes are made.

By taking a step back and re-evaluating the interpretations you've made over your children's health, you begin setting yourself and your child free. This kind of freedom cannot be bought, it can only be felt. Life most certainly has some interesting ways of teaching us things about ourselves that we were unaware of before. This experience is no different. There will be one massive epiphany after massive epiphany when you start allowing life, along with your own guidance, to heal and nurture your child. Often with anxiety sufferers, we give too much advice and provide too much feedback. The connections we've made between worry being equal to good parenting have been in place for far too long and have most likely manifested from being influenced by the behaviors of a parental figure in our own lives. When your child starts to feel like they can open up to you and speak about things that they most likely couldn't have done before, you start to become their best friend once again. If you'd like, you may also choose to be open with them and explain how you became overzealous over their health. This is also a good step forward between you and your children. Of course, you'll most likely have to deal with your own inner child's ideas that if you do open up to them, they may latch onto health anxiety themselves because of your reckless actions. Well, sometimes what feels reckless in the health anxiety world is just a necessary action that needs to be taken to prove to ourselves that a new truth is coming over us. Take these points to heart and understand that stepping back doesn't make you a bad parent, it just shows your new level of emotional maturity.

Chapter 10:
The Fear of Getting Better

I simply couldn't write this essential guide to health anxiety without adding a chapter on the in-depth experience that health anxiety warriors have far too often. This experience is the actual discomfort and fear of getting better. Some of you may think this is silly, that you would do anything to heal the components of what triggers your health anxiety without a second thought. This may be true at a conscious level, but, as we now know very well, the conscious mind doesn't run the show until enough feeling, repetition, and certainty are applied. At the time of writing this book, I posted a question on our Facebook Support Page and the question was:

Is there a part of you that's afraid of getting well?

I'd like to share a few of the answers I received with you below to see if you can relate. Keep in mind, on our Facebook Support Page we are dealing with different forms of anxiety all at different stages of the journey:

"There must be! It didn't seem like it to me, but friends and family are always telling me 'You must like feeling this way.'"

If this response doesn't scream out conflict between the conscious and subconscious mind, I don't know what will.

No one 'likes' feeling this way, everyone has parts to them that want immediate change if at all possible. Here is another answer I received:

"I don't know if it is a fear of getting well or a fear of not being able to get well."

As we can see here, the inner child has provided a defense mechanism in the form of an idea that says 'you are simply not able to get well because …'. This idea has turned into a lingering feeling that sustains a state of fear as well as an addiction to suffering, all comfort zones to the inner child's subconscious mind. I have a feeling this person has negotiated with themselves by using logic many times over, along with friends and family members reminding them that there's no reason why they cannot be well again. Logic, however, often comes with limited capabilities within this convincing game we are playing with our own bodies. Deeper work is necessary.

"I hope I'm not! I want nothing more than to be done with health anxiety. Maybe somewhere deep down, I'm afraid of losing the sense of protection and security that has come with it. Something I should explore further."

The two words that stick out here are 'protection' and 'security'. As we can see, spending enough time associating anxiety with providing a sense of protection and safety has its positives and its negatives. The positives are delusions while the negatives are justified. Anxiety does not protect, it just gives the illusion of protection and security, remember that.

"I keep on stopping right at the the end of your health anxiety program before I finish it because I am afraid. I am afraid that if I finish it and I won't be healed then I will never heal."

Control, a need for certainty, perfectionism, and a fear of the unknown are all at play here. This person most likely does not have a skill set application issue. Rather, they have a mindset issue. Prior to starting any program or method, the person's approach must be with the firm belief that this method will take me somewhere new. Toward newfound wisdom, to new approaches to unfamiliar situations, to new persona parts that want to come out of suppression, and more. Self-made pressure is another one of those tricky defense mechanisms used by the inner child to prolong an anxiety-riddled identity. If you find yourself within the clutches of a 'do or die' type mentality, it's important to take note of when and by whom the core beliefs that accompany this attitude were created. Of course, knowing the answer to this is not enough. Some type of emotional reframing of memories and potentially verbal expression toward this person, or similar personalities which may be present in your present life, may be necessary.

Now let's get one thing straight with all of this: Just because you think in these ways doesn't mean you are weird, strange, crazy, or anything else. Often when we admit such things about ourselves, we fall into a state of even greater fear and franticness out of fear of 'losing it'. You're on a journey, a journey toward deeper understanding. This means that if we can accept that we feel a certain way without allowing ourselves to go any further down the rabbit hole of self-labeling, we are continuing to grow emotionally. When we grow emotionally, we grow into emotional maturity and out of our old fear-focused programming that has led to health anxiety.

When it comes to the fear of getting better, the end goal is to replace it with the fear of not getting better.

If you don't 'clean up your past', work through these illusory negative ideas, upgrade your core belief systems, and step out of the shadow of your mother and father, what then? These are great questions to answer because the answers will cue up the pain button in a better way. Sometimes with health anxiety sufferers you have to agitate the problem and create more pain within them to see what direction their lives are really going. The two ways to motivate someone is through associating a great deal of pain with staying where they are or by associating high amounts of pleasure with what the change will eventually bring. We are associating pain with not changing rather than unconsciously associating it with changing, which is good. When answering this question you will feel a sense of anger, which is also good. This type of anger is transformational rather than self-defeating. This transformational anger will open you up to more information around the health anxiety identity that you've become. This kind of anger will lead you to taking action, unlike the old kind of anger that promoted victimhood.

Feelings will come with this kind of anger, feelings that at one time in your life you associated with physical self-destruction. Now, however, these same feelings aren't connected to illness or disease but to energy, solely energy. This jolt in physical energy can be used to oppose our old suppressive ways and to take daily action to change our mindset and physical habits, or it can be used to prolong fear if not properly addressed. Remember, we're retraining ourselves to see the truths behind ourselves and life. The truths that remind us of a safe, rather than threatening life, the truths that remind us that we are free to believe in anything and do what we wish. One of the most rewarding moments for me is when a person who was once afraid and questioning their healing later comes to me and says that they've made peace with the part of them that was afraid. That part, as we now know is the inner child, starts to form a new relationship between the conscious mind and the unconscious body. I always ask them how they did it, how did they turn their fear of healing into whole-heartedly welcoming healing in. Often their answer is 'I listened and followed what I felt I needed to do'. Many health anxiety sufferers are anxiety masters themselves. They understand in such great detail what anxiety is, how it manifests, and what prolongs it. However, although they may know a lot about anxiety, they don't know much about themselves yet since there are still things they must come to grips with, fears that they must admit that are still lingering, and guilt that still plays a heavy role in their present lives.

Let's say you choose to throw out a chair from your favorite room in your home. What's the initial feeling that you get? Often it's a feeling of emptiness, a feeling that this chair must be replaced with a new one. It is much easier to replace something than it is to delete something or throw something out. This is a crucial lesson in healing health anxiety-related ideas, behaviors, and mental images. Your general approach to the day must be focused on replacing and not on getting rid of. For example, what could a lingering symptom of anxiety mean? It can mean a loving protection coming from the subconscious mind-body. What could a panic attack mean? It could mean that you've allowed an idea to fester and grow into a physiological reaction, which makes the lesson that comes with panic valuable for the future. Replacing goes hand in hand with responding.

Responding to unconscious and irrational fear is a mindset while replacing them is the practical component to healing.

The right attitude will breed the right answers, and the right answers within the context of health anxiety will eventually give way to self-permission. Because isn't self-permission a large piece of this type of healing anyway? To give ourselves wholehearted permission to no longer fear, no longer suppress, no longer hide and distract? This is a wonderful moment on this journey, I can promise you that much. It really is a turning point. Therefore, it's important to understand that age doesn't necessarily translate into wisdom. Just because someone has more life experience than you doesn't mean that their beliefs must be hailed as law. This is an important point when it comes to our parents, in fact, since so many of us are still living under the umbrella of their core beliefs. We can love them (or anyone for that matter) and yet disagree with what they believe is true for us and life in general. Wow, now that is an epiphany if I've ever felt one. When you are at peace with yourself and life you no longer need motivation either, since motivation in my eyes is externally led whereas wisdom is internally led. The wise understand that health anxiety is a chapter in their lives that they are growing out of and there is no need for external motivation to attempt to make inner or behavioral changes. These changes aren't temporary, they are a lifestyle, even if the world wants you to stay as you've always been. These are the kinds of sacrifices that it takes to put a life of worry behind you for good.

Worry can become your best friend if you are not living life consciously and on your own terms.

Not the kind of best friend you want or deserve, however. This relationship with worry can negatively affect every aspect of life and soon enough we may even find ourselves wondering where the time went? People that are living in a state of inner peace don't concern themselves with how fast or slow the time is going since they understand that to do so is to be pulled back into ideas that only strengthen the desire for more control over our lives. Instead, let time be what it may be, whether it moves fast or slow doesn't matter since now within your journey of healing you don't allow yourself to believe everything you feel anyway, right? The words 'don't believe everything you feel' caught on like wildfire within our community while I was writing *F*** Coping, Start Healing* and gave people a chance to question what their minds were saying about what their bodies were doing. These words brought power back to them after feeling so powerless for so long. It broke them out of their trance state of fear and put them in a state of reflection (different from over-analyzing). So for a brief period of time, they reflected on how they got to where they were, which brought on more powerful epiphanies.

Imagine, one line, one sentence that provides this much self-led permission to take life on in a whole new way and to take ourselves and even our bodies less seriously. Yes, we must care for our bodies, we must love our bodies, and we must work with physicians when the time is right to help our bodies. However, we no longer have to be obsessed with our bodies. This translates into a state of trust, and a state of trust diminishes health anxiety faster than anything else I've come across. This state of trust may be met through one sentence as I've mentioned above, or through years of 'messy' reframing work. Either way, it is what it is. We mustn't look to rush our healing or we will succumb to further states of fear and anxiety. Rather, we must open ourselves up to the lessons we need to receive at the time we are meant to receive them. People can only truly receive and take in the wisdom and external support at the time they are meant to. Some of us may have a few other lessons and experiences we must go through before hearing the same message you've been telling them for the past few years. This is neither a good nor a bad thing. It doesn't speak to their character flaws one bit, but rather it speaks to the way life is. Before health anxiety, we were very much lost (even though we may think that these were some of the best times of our lives), during health anxiety we are bewildered, confused, and feel betrayed, and after health anxiety we will be not only relieved but very much enlightened. How far we choose to take that enlightenment is up to each of us. Some may be tempted to stay where they are, while others would rather take this inner journey as far as they can. I have chosen the latter, to take the lessons health anxiety (as well as all the other inner challenges I've come across) has taught me and continue to seek what else could be possible for me. I now become curious when I meet a person who speaks more than they need to and has associated listening to a limitation of some sort toward themselves, for example. During my health anxiety days, I would have loved nothing more than to ask them if they ever experienced this or that bodily symptom. Nowadays I don't reach for any kind of reassurance anymore, but rather allow things to be as they are and let others figure themselves out over time. Of course, I will respectfully speak of what I believe is true for them since I will never shun or suppress my intuition ever again. The way they receive this information, however, is up to them, not up to me. This kind of mindset can really preserve a lot of spiritual and physical energy. By preserving our life force and physical energy we have more to give for what we deemed are the highest priorities in our lives presently. Health anxiety can suck these energies right out of us if we continue to allow it to. I should know after suffering for years prior to healing it.

A person asked me during a podcast interview whether I had any regrets in my life and my answer really surprised me...

My answer was no. 'No regrets at all, Dennis? Not even one?' My inner child reacted briefly. No, I thought, not even one. I wouldn't change the years of living under the rule of a terrorizing father and an overly worrying mother, nor the pressures of having to deal with external things while simultaneously dealing with the most debilitating anxiety daily. This, my friends, is where we are going to get you to; this place. Regret is poison, nothing less and nothing more. It poisons the mind into thinking there will always be something wrong with us and the world, and it poisons the spirit into thinking that life isn't on our side. Life can and will be wonderful once again for you if you are reading this book to heal your health anxiety. I say this because you have already shown your commitment simply by picking up and reading this essential guide. I sense it in you even though we may have never met each other before, because the ones that are healed aren't more capable than you. This is something you may have heard before, only this time you must feel the truth behind these important words.

Chapter 11:
Believing In Your Good Health

A person dealing with health anxiety wants nothing more than to believe that their bodily symptoms are emotionally connected and that their negative mental chatter is just made-up stories and conspiracy theories about themselves. However, what commonly becomes the case is that the more we want something, the farther it gets from us. This idea of willing ourselves to believe in our good health seems to only lead to more question marks around our health. Hoping, wanting, and using willpower only bring with them more questions that will lead to more suffering and are all connected (at an underlying level) to fear. Hope represents the idea that there's just a very small chance of it happening, while the chance of it not happening is, in fact, great. Wanting something to happen often leads to waiting for something to happen, which also connects to the fear of what surprises may arise should it happen. Willpower is a finite resource; we only have a certain amount of it and if you are waking up every day looking to will yourself past the less-than-ideal situations you encounter, you will run out of this resource and find yourself looking for quick fixes once again.

You cannot blame someone dealing with health anxiety for approaching their healing this way, though.

The reason is that living by the rules of a heightened state of survival leads only to a series of frantic reactions to mental, physiological, and environmental challenges. If you are currently in this inner space, you can let go of the guilt around how you've been lately. You certainly know better but are being led by the protective guidelines set forth by your own inner child. Here are two opposing actions we take during health anxiety that only lead to further suffering. They are:

To push, meaning …

- Pray for healing while simultaneously doubting our capabilities to heal
- Wishing for relief toward the day ahead without the mindset of cooperation between the mind and body
- Hoping that others hold the words to heal you
- Over-exposure; physically and energetically depleting yourself through over exertion around your exposure work
- Overbearing and controlling other people's lives since there's the feeling of having little control over your own

Again this is about reflection, not guilt. We are reflecting on habits that we weren't necessarily aware of before that we thought helped but only perpetuated our health anxiety further.

On the opposite side of the scale, there is also to pull (or pull back), meaning …

- To never visit a physician because of the fear of what diagnosis may arise
- To isolate yourself in the hopes that you feel better prior to re-engaging with your creative sides and the world
- To neglect new ideas around good health and refuse to build on the supporting facts, but instead reverting to a familiar place of worry, fear, and anxiety

I will mention many times in this book that the main personal ingredient to healing health anxiety is, and always will be, trust. Trust allows someone dealing with health anxiety to relax more, to believe in something different, and to explore themselves and the world with a newfound level of wonder and certainty. It is a beautiful sight when I witness this in people. They often use the word 'lighter' as in, 'I simply feel lighter'. This lightness is a result of giving themselves permission to devalue worry and to increase the value of living more carefree. Less worry leads to more trust, and more trust leads to the strengthening of our intuition.

These are the signs you must become aware of as you progress through the stages of healing health anxiety for good. The signs come and go as quickly as we choose. However, a person truly invested in increasing their emotional maturity will spend extra time learning to recognize the signs that connect to their progress. No longer will they turn their attention to the next thing to be stimulated by which we now know as being 'distraction action', but rather they welcome and are intrigued by signs of inner progress. When trust is built within this newfound relationship between the conscious and subconscious minds, hardly anything feels like a threat anymore. Rather, any inner challenge brought on by feeling—or thought or even a situational challenge—can easily be dealt with.

Suffering is not a necessary component of a good life.

This reminder is important, as many of us feel like we must suffer to achieve. When speaking of achieving I mean achieving a steady income, a sound relationship, optimal health, or any other personal goals. I'll give you a good example of how I learned this lesson deeply. Many years ago, as I would stay up all night writing books, creating online anxiety recovery programs, and studying people who've recovered from health anxiety, I felt more alive than ever. Many thought that I was sacrificing something and suffering deeply because of the extra time I was spending on understanding anxiety more deeply, when in fact I was thriving because of the time I spent on how to properly heal. I learned that, within the context of anxiety, when we can share the lessons learned with others, we contribute greatly to both ourselves and others. In this case, staying up late at night wasn't suffering at all, but rather a time filled with the satisfaction of progressing toward a purpose I was being led toward. Anything can be enjoyable, even healing from health anxiety, if we can tap into the correct approach, the correct mindset. To not suffer for another day, no matter what stage in the health anxiety healing journey you are on, I suggest resting your attention on what parts of this journey are enjoyable. As you do this more effectively and more often you will find balance between acting on your newfound clarity and taking time to allow things to manifest as they may. This balance is key to getting to the next step on the healing ladder. To act and to allow is the real task when it comes to 'responding' work. As trust is built, life will begin to slow down in all aspects and you will have the chance to catch up on what's taking place in the present, rather than rush to a future that is already pre-determined by your protective subconscious mind body. The issue with health anxiety isn't so much to live in the present moment more since we are, in fact, often very much in the present handling the threats coming from the mind and the body. But rather, the issue is to live in the present in a different way. In a way where we can differentiate a replayed thought from a conscious thought, and in a way where we can feel a bodily symptom and connect our suppressed feelings to what the body is sharing with us through the symptoms.

At any given moment at any time of the day, no matter where we are, we have the option to believe in something that defies the illusion of an immediate threat.

Simply feeling that a new core belief system is available to us often leads us to the 'right' action for that moment. Too often people who are looking for health anxiety healing search for something to do about it rather than search for how to approach it. It's the correct approach, the correct state of mind, that will lead to a more understanding relationship between mind and body. It is this new attitude that will bring about answers that we were once blocked off from. Like the clouds that cover the sun, our life motto determines whether the clouds will part so we can witness the sun and all its wisdom and benefits once again. A life motto that has been built up through the will of others that says that 'life is a long dark tunnel' or 'life is a painful journey' will only lead to mental limitations. However, a life motto that says 'life is an adventurous roller coaster ride which honors curiosity' will in turn lead to mental flexibility.

When I altered my own life motto and consciously reminded myself of it with repetition and feelings of being present, I encountered more and more moments of clarity. I began feeling like I was seeing life differently than everyone else. They saw life as a few daily routines that played out consistently from day to day and nothing beyond that. I started seeing life through infinite possibilities and potentials and in turn, the obsessiveness over my body was no more. Over time the body became secondary to the spirit for me (and many others who deem themselves as being healed). This provides much comfort to those that have a debilitating fear of death; knowing that the spirit lives on and that the body is just a temporary vessel that we use in this lifetime to gather specific lessons.

Any idea can become a truth for us if we believe in it wholeheartedly.

This important concept leads to a question you must ask yourself repeatedly: what idea must you adopt for this particular challenge that brings you back to a neutral emotional state? Not excited nor afraid, but neutral, since it is within this neutral state where intuition has the best chance to decide for us. Ideas are just that, ideas. That is, until we choose to believe in them. To get to a place of deep trust you must be very picky as to which ideas you accept and which you reject. Someone one morning may decide to affect you with their ideas by saying 'it's an awfully cloudy day, isn't it?' Knowing that the subconscious mind takes everything literally, if you agree to this statement through the energy of words it will lead to a greater possibility that you will accept the next negative statement you hear as well.

Every idea accepted into the subconscious mind makes the potential for the next similar idea to be accepted at a deep level, and even more so if it has something to do with your health. Soon enough, we automatically attribute cloudy days to being awful days and we choose to isolate ourselves within the confines of our comfort zones when it's cloudy. We don't question this idea and where it originally came from very often. This kind of reflection work only arises after we've suffered enough emotionally and are ready to make some much-needed changes. When we were young children, a cloudy day didn't mean good or bad, but it always meant opportunity, like an opportunity for rain, which created puddles to jump into. The distinction between good and bad came later on but it was built up over time. Likewise, to trust in our anxiety symptoms as being emotional messengers leaves us feeling vulnerable at the start. We feel that if we do adopt this approach there would be a potential to miss a physical ailment in the making and therefore it may get worse over time. Like other ideas, this idea will continue to build over time as we struggle between the need for control and immediate answers and leaving it alone.

Remember, you have the power to believe anything about anything or anyone.

The only thing holding you back are the stories your inner child tells you that you may experience should you begin believing in something new. There's the inner child's defense mechanism once again front and center (as it will be regularly until these new ideas become law for us and within us). The most satisfying moment of clarity for me came when I finally realized that the bodily symptoms and sensations that come and go are normal. A little body zap here, a tightness in the throat there. These normal sensations used to take me down a rabbit hole of fear and dread until I realized later on in my healing journey that they were simply things that the body does from time to time. When I was dealing with health anxiety, the reason why I was so afraid of these symptoms and sensations was because of my total fixation on my body 24 hours a day even while asleep (the inner child never sleeps, but rather always looks after us). The absolute fixation on my body showed a lack of trust, and a lack of trust led me away from thinking (rather than replaying thoughts). It's all connected, and it all connects to more and more anxiety. There comes a point where living without feeling suffocated by any form of anxiety and all that comes with it daily feels too strange to bear. If this isn't the definition of the addiction to suffering, I'm not sure what is.

I do believe that regular check-ups are important for the maintenance of good physical health. I will also say that if something feels bothersome, do get a second opinion as to what it may mean. However, keep in mind that if during the check up something does arise, such as a blood pressure issue, remind yourself that if your blood pressure was checked earlier that day it may very well have read normal. Sometimes the lead up to a situation can play tricks on the body. You are in a highly sensitized state while at the check-up, along with being in a conflicted state with your subconscious mind. Do not fret, no matter the diagnosis, as often these are just calls to action to take a deeper look at your unresolved feelings. Stress and anxiety, especially health anxiety, are not a healthy or protective way to live. The constant feeling of being on guard makes us believe that danger lurks around every corner, when in fact what's behind every corner is nothing more than a fly that we've convinced ourselves could be a threat to our lives. Over time we begin leaving the fly alone rather than give off the frequency of fear, hence the distance that begins forming between that fly and ourselves.

Another example is this:

Imagine a robber who late at night is walking down a dark alleyway hoping to rob someone of their valuables. The robber spots a group of 3 people walking side by side. The first person is giving off a 'pleasant frequency' enjoying the night sky and the brisk air. The second person is giving off a 'connected frequency' as they feel a positive and deep connection to the other two people. The third person is giving off a 'what if' frequency that is deeply connected to the fear of what could take place in that alleyway. The robber, intuitive as they may be from years of robbing, senses the fear-led frequency emanating from the person's tight walking posture, which is again connected to their shallow breathing rhythm, and chooses this person as their victim because they are the one giving off this electromagnetic signal. Some may deem this as being a coincidence. However, those that pick up on patterns within this life experience won't. The 'what if' person is robbed, which leads to them creating another confirmation for themselves—that walking in the alley at night-time is at the top of the list in terms of a threat to their physical health.

To some degree, we all know deep down that we shouldn't walk in an alleyway late at night. However, this is just an example of three different people all being conscious of three different things. One was aware of the beauty of that particular night, the other had a sense of gratitude for the people they were with, and the third person was distracted by a fear of what could potentially happen. The deeper the feeling, the more detailed the mental movie. The more detailed the mental movie, the greater the signal that is being sent out into the world as to what we want to happen. This doesn't mean that you must always be in a pleasant state to live a life of inner peace and balance. It only means that you must pay more attention to the components in life that eventually lead to the result, the feeling. Often we think that a feeling is law, and whatever we feel we must act on. Not necessarily. Take health anxiety, for example. Just because you feel like your dizziness is connected to a brain disease doesn't mean that it is. To question a feeling is to re-route where your attention gets placed, and once you do this repeatedly the feeling begins to mean something else, something real. In this case, the dizziness starts to become a message of physical depletion, unresolved childhood trauma, or suppressed anger toward your father, for example. It could mean all of them even, which in turn begs the question of 'where would I even get started with all this new information?' The best place to start is with your newfound relationship with your body, that's what I believe. Your body doesn't hate you; it only looks to protect you in some way, shape, or form. For far too long we have treated our bodies like a trash can, eating foods that we are not meant to be eating, or verbalizing thoughts we should not be verbalizing.

Honestly, do you love all that your body is?

I'm not talking about just the 'good times' you spend with your body, I'm talking about the challenges as well. Do you nurture your body with vitamins and mineral-rich foods? Do you get adequate sleep nightly? Are you lessening the negative emotional weight you've been carrying all this time in your body through reframing practices? How do you speak to your body daily? Our life experience very much comes down to the relationship between our consciousness and our bodies. For far too long I cared more for others than I did for myself. I gave away sound advice but never used it since my level of self-worth was so low at the time. However, you and I are both worthy of an optimally healthy life experience in mind, body, and spirit. Health anxiety is a means to an end, an experience that demands lessons be learned so that new life experiences can be brought to you. Therefore you mustn't doubt yourself or sense that you will be living with health anxiety forever. You've begun to tap into some lessons from the past and it's important that you see them now and don't repeat them. The biggest lesson, I believe, was that you doubted yourself. Since the doubt holds no factual support, it is in actuality just an idea that we've given too much power over to. I believe in you and soon you will begin to believe in yourself. Until then, stay focused on building trust in your infinite potentials and love that body of yours like you never have before, warrior.

Chapter 12:
The Biggest Lesson: Reframing

I always had a feeling that goal setting while you were the wrong kind of person to manifest your desires was wrong. To set a goal while sending out the feeling signals of fear and doubt will only lead to more frustration and lack of trust in life within you. When we set goals at a time when we are making great progress within our health, the momentum will carry us toward the next step in making that goal a reality for us. As a health anxiety warrior uncovers the roots of the emotional weight they've been carrying around in their bodies for so long, they begin to see how one relationship and experience has led to the next. This is less of a mental investigative journey as it is an intuitive, feeling-out journey, as we feel out the root causes of our conscious and unconscious blocks today. As this continuous inner work evolves, what must we become progressively more aware of? That is what we will focus on in this chapter; when fear becomes acceptance and past experience is truly seen as a past experience, nothing more.

There can be no healing without some form of expression.

I hope this message has become clear to you at this point in the book. Mental expression in the form of giving priority to new meanings around things and verbal expression as we speak up in times where we feel pulled to do so, are both necessary to align ourselves with our new identity, and our higher selves. Behavioral expressions, on the other hand, are the new actions we take that connect to our default ways of doing things. Waking up and going straight to your phone to check how many likes your latest post received, for example, may not align with your goals for health anxiety recovery (even though this action isn't connected to health in any way, there is still a deeper connection to fear). However, the action of going for a walk while emphasizing an empowered posture and breathing pattern does align with our goals for healing and personal growth. The interesting thing is, when you feel you are in the health anxiety healing process you implement these actions without needing to know what the result may be, knowing that you can handle it no matter what. There is a sense of looking forward to a deeper form of personal exploration rather than overly focusing on the consequences of your new action. Even if you become aware of the old bodily symptoms that still linger, you aren't as bothered by them. You just know that in time the body will release the stronghold of the emotional connection to these physical symptoms, so you stay on the path that you feel is right for you. If you are at this stage in your healing then great, and if you are not quite here yet that's fine as well. There are still things you must come to grips with and learn from in order to progress to this level of inner momentum, and that is okay. As difficult as your current personal situation may be, don't rush the healing process. Because if you look to skip steps, you'll only have to go back in time and reexamine them. You are exactly where you need to be and going through what you need to go through—this approach is crucial for bringing harmony between the subconscious and conscious minds.

There is a big difference between coping with and healing health anxiety, here's an example of both ...

When looking to cope with your bodily symptoms and the label of health anxiety there is an unconscious discomfort in getting rid of them. The bond, although exhausting and debilitating, has provided a sense of protection for us and therefore the uncertainty of 'healing' seems to always be lingering. Coping with health anxiety is like preparing for a date in your own home when your home is a complete mess. You take everything in your home and stuff them as high as possible into any closet you can find since your date most likely will not be too interested in what is in your closet and won't look there. Your house may look tidy and put together, but in the back of your mind you know that it isn't and know that as soon as you reopen your closet the mess will just come back again. How can one have a clear mind and an open heart during this date knowing that they are, in a sense, lying to the person they are meeting with? So yes, you desire freedom from the components of health anxiety and freedom from the label itself, but it is not until the physical experience takes a backseat to the mental experience of seeing things from a more energetic perspective that we begin trusting in the new emotional connections we are making.

Coping with health anxiety is connected to hanging onto old associations with your past relationships. Not only with them, however, but with yourself as well. If you see things the same way you will rarely get to experience new feelings. For these new feelings of inner peace to arise as your new default response, you must understand that healing is separate to coping. Which one do you feel like you are more engaged in at this point in your journey? Do you feel like you are babysitting your bodily symptoms and entertaining your catastrophic ideas too much? Or do you feel like you are starting to move beyond these time-wasting habits?

Bruce Lee said it best, "Be like water, my friend."

This is, of course, the end goal, to 'be like water'. We must first become like mud before we become like water though, I believe. Mud is messy, it often has a bad odor to it, and it isn't very desirable to look at. You can consider yourself 'in the mud' while the mind creates its new associations with your past experiences and relationships, new associations to your bodily symptoms, and engages in bodily acts of purging such as sweating, crying, and even shaking while engaged in some form of reframing practice. Often it is the person themselves who unknowingly keeps themselves in mud for longer than they need to. Without realizing it, they feel a deep pull to stay at least somewhat focused on their body, entertaining their catastrophic thoughts. I lived in this place for a long time before I had finally suffered enough. What I thought was connected to caring for my body was only living by the protective beliefs of my inner child. I thought I was doing what was best for me by continuing to engage in habits that kept my health anxiety alive. Little did I realize at the time, however, was that all I was doing was getting the opposite result of what I truly wanted, which was sound mental, emotional, physical, and spiritual health.

Take a moment right now before reading on to recognize what the biggest lesson is for you here and now based on what you have just read in this chapter.

When we become 'like water', life itself and even death take on a whole new meaning. We are neither afraid of the unfamiliar experiences that life may present to us, nor are we connected to the same association we once had about death. Interestingly, many health anxiety recoverers find themselves led to some form of spiritual or religious practice that reflects the idea that the spirit lives on. What a wonderful way of approaching the uncertainties of death that bring so much pain to a person daily. With this kind of association, you can freely live and provide yourself further permission to make up your own mind as to the meaning of anything. When coping with health anxiety we view a past traumatic memory as being a 'bad' thing and look to engage in 'distraction action'. While healing, we see the same experience from a neutral angle and form an emotionally-led response. As the inner child brings up this past traumatic memory, it is simultaneously asking the question of 'do we still look at this the same way we always have?' and 'is there a new meaning now?' In that very moment, if we can address our full attention and energy to the memory that was brought up and provide it with a new meaning, we are then guiding the inner child away from the addiction to suffering and toward a new way of experiencing life. You must understand that there is no such thing as a good or bad memory, feeling, or thought. What was once a bad memory can become an experience we once encountered, a bad feeling can become a protective message from the inner child, and a bad thought can become connected to old habitual ways of thinking.

If you are just being introduced to these new approaches to healing health anxiety for the first time today, you will not be very good at them. There will be excuses that arise as to why this is too hard, how you are incapable, etc. These excuses must be dismissed and seen as nothing more than protective mechanisms inspired by your subconscious mind that is looking to keep you in a familiar and therefore comfortable state of irrational fear. Often we give up on ourselves too soon and on the new mindsets and techniques we encounter too easily, and find ourselves starting over again and again 'trying' this and trying that. These don't signify a lack of determination, but rather the lack of the right mindset or a lack of skill sets combined with being disconnected from the end result. When the end result is in the form of a mental picture (or movie) and it is as big as an IMAX movie theatre with stunning colors and vibrant sound, there can be no giving up on the process of healing. To persevere becomes natural as long as we are reminded of what we are persevering towards. Keeping that image in your mind as you go about your health anxiety healing work will even lead to a sense of gratitude over having and healing health anxiety, since the lessons learned will only be molding you into the kind of person that can much more easily manifest the good things they desire into their lives. Change your default way of feeling and you change the energetic output you are sharing with the world. Once this is altered for the better, there's no telling what good will come your way. You just have to have the faith to jump in with a full heart.

Uncovering and reframing 'the mess' is a lifelong journey.

As long as we understand this, we will continue to move beyond health anxiety each time. We tend to consider a new bodily symptom (or lingering one) as a setback. But what if there's another explanation to it that we haven't considered yet? The body is 100% memory; your symptoms are 100% memory. For example, recently as I was helping to clean up the past with one client, we realized that her lingering symptom, the lump in their throat, kept her in a state of perpetual fear. As I brought her into a calmer state where we had deeper access to the subconscious mind, she told me that she sensed that this bodily symptom had everything to do with her inability to speak up to her parents when they fought. She wanted so deeply for them to get along, to stop arguing. However, as a young child, she mentioned that she felt powerless to help them see another way past their disagreements. While in that state of suggestibility I asked her to imagine herself courageously speaking up, out loud, to her parents. She did so, and you could tell how badly she needed this moment in order to move forward. The tears came pouring down and as she reached for the tissues, I reminded her that we wouldn't be suppressing those tears back into the body today, and encouraged her to let everything be as they may. I asked her, is there anything else you'd like to share with your parents at that very moment? She answered yes, she wanted to let them know that even though she disagreed with them in terms of how life should be lived, she still loved them.

We mustn't wait for time to heal the components that have led us to our health anxiety. Rather, when something that has activated health anxiety arises, we must become curious about it and take time to understand its message more deeply than we ever have before. I've just shared with you one way of emotionally reframing a memory, and that is by first calming the mind and body, asking what the physical symptom of anxiety is connected to, going with the intuitive answer, and expressing what needed expression at a time when we weren't capable or allowed to (childhood). This is the baseline of my work, to bring resolve to peoples' memories that connect to physical symptoms. You can begin doing this deeper work yourself without the need for guidance from anyone (or should you choose, head to the 'reframing' playlist on my YouTube channel). Meditation, grounding, forest bathing, massages, and warm baths will all have a big effect on bringing balance between your intuition and intelligence as well. A common mistake we tend to make is to think that meditation alone will heal health anxiety when in fact often it only leads to uncovering the things that have kept us stuck all this time. The same goes with the other calming practices I've just mentioned; they are to be used to get to the root cause of the problem and not to solve the problem directly. Calming the nerves often only has a temporary effect on the mind and body, not a lasting one. However, when meditation (focusing on one), reframing (bringing resolve to past memories and suppressed emotions), and responding (in the moment of fear work) are all used on a daily basis, there is no limit to what can be healed.

Once you find yourself expressing yourself fearlessly and more often, you will know yourself to be on the healing path.

Most health anxiety sufferers I've come across in the last decade have referred to themselves as 'introverts' and live by this label. I believe they (as I had done as well in my past) are more so hiding behind this label rather than looking more deeply into it. Further along in this healing journey, we all reach a place where we embrace our alone time more and more. However, this isn't the same as being an introvert. Being introverted has more to do with protection than an identity. If we continue to see ourselves in this fashion, we will continue to lead a life of suppression rather than expression. To varying degrees, we are social creatures that crave connection and appreciation. This doesn't mean you must associate yourself with being an extrovert at this point in your healing, it only means that you must ask yourself better questions, such as 'what am I most deeply afraid of?'

Rejection is usually at the top of most people's list until they realize that the ones who once rejected them were mostly just caught up with unresolved feelings from their own past relationships.

There is no peace in always looking to please others while putting yourself last on the list, there is only suffering. As you continue to uncover the root causes of your health anxiety with openness and patience, you will find that you don't need to identify with any label whatsoever. Rather, the only question you must answer is 'who do I need to be right now in order to continue on my healing path?' When you are true to the answer and act in line with it, you will have taken another giant step forward toward wisdom and purpose. In essence, no you are not an introvert nor are you an extrovert. Rather, you are a human being that gets to choose which 'persona parts' will show up at which time. Freedom from health anxiety will not look the way you think it will. There won't be a big celebration at the end of all of this. You may not even realize that you've put it behind you for good. You will, however, have a smile from ear to ear and a recognition of true inner growth.

There will be a moment of deep proudness as newfound wisdom enters your mind.

Keep looking to plant the seed of curiosity within your inner distress. The path ahead may feel long but I promise you, it is shorter than you had once perceived. Soon, you will look back and see how far you've come, how you've left a world of irrational fear for a world of childlike wonder. These are the true signs of healing.

Chapter 13:
Understanding The Inner Child's Connections

One of the most eye-opening ways I began understanding my own inner child was to ask it to produce the feelings of:

- Failure
- Doubt
- Fear
- Love
- Joy
- Neutrality

I did this while I was in an alpha/theta brainwave state which allowed me to understand more deeply the beliefs held by my own inner child/subconscious mind. The results were very interesting. When I asked my inner child to produce the feelings of failure, doubt, and fear, within a split second I had tapped into all the facts that supported these feelings, and there I was, deep with each of them. When I asked it to produce the feelings of love, I immediately felt undeserving of this feeling (mainly stemming from a father figure that needed me to prove a result before feeling a good feeling). I could only go so far with love before hitting an emotional barrier that didn't allow me to go any further into the feeling. With love, I also felt anger. I believe this stemmed from my observations as a child as my parents verbally fought, and since they were my models of love, I had unconsciously attributed the feeling of fighting, revenge, rage, etc. to my feeling of love. When I asked the inner child to produce the feelings of joy, at the time I thought of my newborn son who in fact gave me life—hence naming him Hayat, which means 'life' in the Turkish language. Soon enough, however, joy turned to worry since worry was my good friend and my relationship with worry at the time was very comforting and safe. Joy was quite fleeting as a feeling, and my inner child wouldn't allow it to be present for too long out of a need to revert back to the familiar feeling of fear. Finally, I asked the inner child to bring up feelings of neutrality. At first, neutrality felt empty, dark even. But it wasn't necessarily 'bad', it was just a feeling that I wasn't familiar with (which we commonly interpret in a bad way). This was followed up with a feeling of peace within me. I liked it. But just as any relationship takes time to blossom, so did my relationship with emotional neutrality need time to develop.

What I took away from this experience was that what we think of consciously when it comes to these positive and negative feelings is a lot different than how the inner child thinks and interprets them unconsciously.

What does this mean in terms of health anxiety healing? It means that starting today we can begin questioning the feelings that we feel and placing our own connections to them altogether. Here is how it usually goes within the health anxiety cycle:

1) A feeling arises
2) We become consciously aware of the feeling
3) We place a self-sabotaging meaning over the feeling
4) The feeling attaches to worry
5) We look for support from someone else online or consult a physician
6) We receive the confirmation that this is an emotionally-led experience and that we are physically healthy
7) We reflect on how frustrating it is to live with health anxiety
8) We begin questioning the advice and support we received, and in doing so question our health once again
9) We detach from the world around us and are consumed with the world on the inside
10) The cycle continues

That is, until we realize that the fastest and most effective way to prove safety to the subconscious mind/body is right after step 2, the moment when we become aware of the very thing that used to send us spiraling into health anxiety and even panic. At step 2 the feeling can be reversed, and the idea that once supported the feeling can be exposed for what it truly is, a lie to bring us back into a familiar and worrying state of being. It's the same when you first meet someone new. The first meeting, those initial moments are what we remember most powerfully. Later on in the relationship, we are always asked, 'how did you meet your husband or wife?' and with incredible accuracy, we can explain those very moments to anyone at any time. By exploring this more deeply within your relationship with your own subconscious mind, you'll find your greatest opportunity for change resides within the initial moments you feel something or have an unconscious idea pop up. Your actions within those very moments (responding) will be remembered most profoundly by your own inner child, hence it will want to repeat them. This is how life in general works. The more awareness we can bring to moments that we are growing tired of experiencing repeatedly, the faster we can learn the lessons we need to learn in order for those experiences not to happen again, and the faster we can reverse the ideas and feelings. That 10-second window you have between experiencing a 'negative' feeling and placing a new meaning (or behavior) behind it is key. It will feel like the strangest thing you've ever done, and this strange feeling is good. It's a sign that positive change is in the works. In fact, you must chase these strange and vulnerable feelings every chance you get, since they hold the key to balancing out your threat perception with safety over time.

Let's dive a little deeper into understanding your own inner child so that we can turn those worrying feelings into something more neutral as quickly as possible:

1. The inner child never lies – It always represents the truth behind your core beliefs that are then experienced as feelings in the body and unconscious actions.

The inner child always speaks the truth based on what you truly believe. What we believe at a subconscious level affects our brain's filter system, which allows in certain external information, driven by our 5 senses, while disallowing others. For example, we may only see the poster at the bus stop that mentions how kidney dysfunction can be treated only by a certain drug being pushed by Big Pharma, while not seeing the two people kissing on the other side of the street. Why? Because the brain's filter system, driven by our inner child's belief systems, is the driving force deciding what information is allowed in.

Consider our auditory functions. We wake up in the morning focusing highly on the sounds of the traffic while not recognizing the birds chirping in the tree right next to us. Again, these are the filters that run our perceptions. Since the inner child is so highly invested in protecting what it believes to be true, anger over sensing the traffic outside keeps us in a state of fight or flight more rapidly than focusing on the birds chirping. Hence, we stay in a state of over-stimulation and dissatisfaction which maintains our familiar identity connected to anxiety.

We see, hear, feel, taste, and smell, what the inner child allows.

Your health anxiety-filled life you're living today is no accident. But rather, it is the result of a constructive and tedious process led by your own subconscious mind. When you get the sense that the inner child is leading your decision making over your conscious mind, it is imperative that you understand that these feelings are behind your core beliefs. To think, imagine, speak, and act based on a feeling only strengthens the fear you hold within you. However, when we act in defiance of these fear-led core beliefs, we are manifesting a new direction for our lives, since fresh new action is one of the most important factors in healing health anxiety. As we reflect on our actions, we can sense which actions are automated ones generated by the beliefs of the inner child and which are conscious actions generated by the rational mind. For example, hesitancy toward adding meditation to your daily habits can be viewed as defiance toward your core beliefs, nothing more. It's not that you can't meditate, it's that the action itself may take you out of the pattern of 'standing guard' toward your bodily symptoms, which may then lead to a threat becoming realized.

Often we use the words 'I can't' to justify not doing something new for ourselves (especially things that are beneficial). We must discard these words and instead recognize that as we work with these feelings looking to prevent us from this new action, we'll eventually get to a place of agreement between the inner child and conscious mind. This type of faithful consistency will lead to altering our core beliefs to fit with our current conscious beliefs. Soon enough, your behaviors will represent an identity molded in playfulness, lightness, inner peace, and optimism rather than one that represents fear. I suggest that you listen intently when the inner child represents its beliefs through a feeling, a bodily sensation, or unconscious action rather than look to act in line with it. This will stop you in your tracks and end the progression of fear that only leads to heightened health anxiety. No longer are you led by what the inner child deems is truth based on your interpretations created during childhood. Rather, you are embracing the inner positive messiness within a relationship that is just starting to unfold differently.

You don't have to believe what the inner child believes anymore.

2. The inner child's expressions are subtle, at least at first prior to us consciously believing it and acting on its interpretations of threat.

Very sneakily, the inner child makes us believe that what we are doing for our safety is necessary. The health anxiety habits of waking up and checking in to see if bodily symptoms are present may become habitual, however, the habit doesn't have to continue into more deeply ingrained habits.

Health anxiety can become a lifestyle if we do not pay more close attention.

In that very moment that spurs on health anxiety, be direct and firm with your inner child. This new direction is vital for the sake of your new future identity. Tell the feeling within that the bodily symptom can stick around for as long as it wants but it will certainly not lead you toward what it wants for you (isolation). These symptoms are present to isolate you from potential danger. Danger, from the inner child's perspective, is everywhere! It is within the strangers you meet, the creativity you give focus to, the new driving path you are using to get to work, the new diet you're implementing, etc. 'Better safe than sorry' is the idea from this perspective. Your bedroom (often) holds little to no threat to your life or social status, the outside world, however, holds too many unfamiliar and potentially unsafe environments and situations (hence the symptoms). Commonly with health anxiety these types of feelings, ideas, and sensations start subtle and grow in strength and consistency as we apply more focus and energy to them.

Depending on how identified you are with the health anxiety identity, these messages may still be quite subtle (most common) or they can be louder, potentially affecting you throughout each moment of life. Yes, brief breaks are possible from health anxiety but they are few and far between for someone stuck in the grips of the inner child's protective ways. I'm a big believer, however, that the length and severity of your health anxiety matter very little when it comes to healing. Yes, these could be facts that the inner child uses to keep you in a familiar state of suffering, however, the right mindset coupled with a few emotionally gripping techniques have the potential to turn everything around. Keep in mind how much effort it takes to maintain the protection that is health anxiety now. It takes work! I bet you never realized how much conscious and unconscious effort it takes to maintain this state of being. If only you could take the same amount of emotional and behavioral investment and put it into the creation of a new and free you, as I'm sure you are already doing.

The directions and decisions by your inner child are mostly subtle, it's the conscious parts of us that make them more evident and louder over time.

The people in the world that don't suffer from health anxiety don't feed into it. This is most certainly an end goal that is met after the mindset and skill sets within this book are familiar to a point of working harmoniously daily together. To tell a health anxiety sufferer to 'not feed into it' would in my eyes be deemed as lazy advice. The process of healing will lead to this result. To advise someone suffering to use this as a practical practice will only lead to further guilt since so much mental and emotional investment has already gone into this anxiety identity. Let's instead not be so consumed by not being able to divert our attention away from the components of health anxiety and focus more on building the relationship between the unconscious and the conscious. The result of this mindset can only lead to enjoying the process of healing. This in turn boosts the amount of oxytocin (hormone) in your body, which in turn adds to neuroplasticity (the way in which the brain reframes old associations to create new ones).

3. The inner child is always the first to react in any given situation.

Allow a child to step foot into a candy store and they will instantly tell you what they want and show you how happy they are. The same goes for your own inner child. In any given situation, what you feel or which idea you get initially will show you what the inner child thinks about it. Someone dealing with health anxiety steps into a crowded auditorium and will most likely feel a sense of overwhelm and panic as to how far they may have to sit from the exit doors, just in case. Or we get stuck in traffic and are surrounded by cars at every turn as our body begins letting us know of its displeasure with the situation through heightened bodily symptoms of anxiety.

These initial reactions aren't so much a physical threat as they are situational ones.

They come with the idea of 'what if'. The ensuing feelings of panic motivate us even further to give in to the orders from the inner child to leave the situation pronto. What if, however, we felt those initial feelings, understood deeply where they came from (most important), brought compassion toward them, and slowly re-introduced ourselves to the situation. Well, over time what would happen is the initial perceptions of threat would gradually turn into perceptions of safety, not by how much change you created from a mental perspective, but from a physiological one. Here are the 4 keys to physiological change that can be implemented as 'responding' skill sets within those first few seconds of anxiousness:

Posture – To slump is to constrict, to constrict will lead to shallow breathing, which will activate the fight or flight mechanism within us. However, a posture that represents safety will bring about perceptual neutrality which opens the door to over-riding our inner child's perspectives with our conscious ones. Head up, shoulders back, spine upright. I highly recommend wearing a posture corrector, which you can find online if you feel that your willpower may be too diminished at the moment to remind yourself to tweak your posture during moments of feeling challenged.

Breathing patterns – The longer your exhale the safer your inner child will feel. If, however, your inhale is longer than your exhale, you will fall for the fear-based interpretation of your inner child. I highly recommend focusing on a 4-second inhale through your nose and a 6-second exhale through your mouth in those very moments when you have an initial reaction of fear. This will signal the part of your autonomic system that represents resting and digesting and will lead to the interpretation of safety and calm.

Speed – We touched on speed a little earlier in the book. It's vital that you understand its importance even further within those initial moments of hesitation and sensitivity. Your level of sensitivity toward a present or future situation must be respected and not mentally justified since it is solely an interpretation. Yes, your body is more highly sensitive during this chapter in your life, but your speed doesn't have to reflect it. When mentioning speed, I'm referring to how fast you walk, drive, speak, use hand gestures, look around, eat, drink, pretty much everything. However, you won't be able to slow down all these things at once, so it's important to only focus on one aspect of slowing down your speed at any given moment. Take for example a lunch date with a coworker you don't know very well; you would focus on slowing down how fast you eat and chew your food. As time went on you could turn your focus to how fast your verbal communication is and correct it to match the safety perceptions you want your inner child to adopt. Speed is one of the most important components to healing health anxiety for good and demands some type of reminder and consistency in its application. You can draw the letter S on the back of your hand if you choose, and when people ask you about it, be honest and proud of why it is there. Expression is healing while suppression is suffering, so why not take another massive step on your journey at the same time anyway.

Power poses – Power poses come in a number of varieties. My favorites are the victory pose (both hands up in achievement of something meaningful to you) and the wonder-woman pose (hands on hips looking to the side with confident certainty). Holding these poses for a minimum of 2 minutes amplifies oxytocin, decreases feelings of fear, and, within the context of health anxiety, has the potential of turning our fears into seeing the feelings as simply energy. This last point is huge, because once we can change the meaning of our anxiousness, we can start using it for our benefit rather than allowing it to bring us back into hiding behind our health anxiety identity and suppressing our feelings. Practice these poses in front of a mirror and if you feel like you look silly, great! Better to look and feel silly for a few moments each day and heal rather than keep doing what you're doing and receive the same results you are. When coupled with targeted affirmations for specific areas of the body, these power pose moments become that much more powerful in programming our neurology. If you're in a busy environment and want to implement a power pose, just head to the closest bathroom, lock the door in the stall, and power pose!

Within the safe world that we currently live in, rarely do we find ourselves needing to react to a true threat to our lives. We may convince ourselves that some aspects of life are threatening, but who is really doing the convincing here? Certainly not your experienced conscious mind, since it understands the difference between rational and irrational fears. I'm a big believer in mindset, and simply by realizing the power behind these types of 'responding' practices within those initial moments of fear, you are already setting the stage for positive change. Mindset comes before skill set, remember that, and often your intuition will guide you toward the best type of response to irrational fear the more you trust in it.

Instincts are aggressive, intuition is gentle.

Once you understand the difference between instinct and intuition and apply your newfound understanding, you will find yourself getting less caught up in the moment and more 'in the flow' with the current situation. Within this level of heightened consciousness, the distinctions between good and bad take a back seat to ideas around it all being connected to life, experience, and chapters within your healing journey. The gentler we become toward ourselves the greater the chance to hear the fruitful messages of our intuition. I have a feeling that for so long rigidity in thinking and perfectionism in behavior have overtaken your daily life. This may be causing you to become more and more controlling over yourself and even others. This kind of life turns the idea of uncertainty into something negative, even though it was uncertainty that was the driving force behind our wonder as young children. We didn't need to know how something would unfold, we simply trusted. Now we are building back that trust once again.

As Picasso once beautifully said, and I paraphrase here; 'we spend the first half of our adult lives learning to be adults, and the second half learning to be children once again.'

One of the biggest game changers in re-building my core beliefs and re-connecting with my own inner child was taking myself out on dates. When I introduced this idea to friends, they thought I was completely 'losing it', but over time they saw how meaningful this act was. I would take my inner child out for dinner dates, specifically on Sunday evenings, since the start of the work week on Monday usually brought with it a host of catastrophic ideas that tend to become self-fulfilling prophecies. With these catastrophic ideas around how I would function in the upcoming week came heightened anxiety symptoms (a debilitating combination for even the strongest-willed warriors). As you take your inner child out for a date, you don't necessarily have to speak to them verbally. However, it is extremely helpful to mentally and physiologically communicate with them before, during, and after the date. Before, you could let them know all the wonderful and safe things about the environment you're about to enter. During, you could focus on how good the food tastes and how friendly the service is. Afterwards, you could focus on how proud you are of your inner child for being open to such an experience.

Changes such as these that get put into practice consistently will never be forgotten by the inner child.

You can rest assured that this experience will be held within your subconscious mind for the next time a similar experience happens. One wonderful step at a time, you are progressing hand in hand with your own inner child toward inner peace and away from irrational fear. You are influencing the deepest parts of you, rather than being influenced. There are always safety messages connected to your symptoms as well as the plateau we hit in our own healing journeys. When we've proven to our own subconscious minds that we've learned that lesson and continue to act in accordance with the learning of the lesson, the tight grip that presents itself through the body can be let go. A man afraid to carry on a conversation with a waiter in time does so comfortably, hence the release of the lump in the throat feeling connected to a fear of expression. The woman who feels fatigued and constantly mentions how she feels like she's carrying the weight of the world on her shoulders begins to say no to others and puts her self-care as priority number 1, feeling like her energy and vitality are coming back. The person who feels like they're always being watched, triggering emotions connected largely to muscle twitches and shakiness, gives up the need to feel approved by others. In turn, the symptoms subside over time, and they begin feeling like they no longer need the approval from anyone but themselves. This is what's possible for you, my friend. Soon enough your inner child may even become your favorite person to spend time with. This is when the perception of loneliness changes into pleasantness. This is when a person no longer ever feels alone but rather loves their own company. Be warned, however, that your friends may find you a little bit on the strange and distant side, but that's okay though, since now you can weed out the people in your life that only depleted your energy reserves and give priority to those that truly understand and appreciate your journey.

Chapter 14:
Self-Care Time

Within health anxiety healing, the components learned in this book connected to reframing the past (imagery-based practices while in a slow brainwave state) and responding effectively in the moment of anxiousness are very important. However, it's also vital that you recognize the importance of self-care work for the reframing and responding work to be effective enough to clear old negative perceptions and feelings. Many people often think of self-care as selfishness and believe they constantly need to put others before them. However, without self-care how can you care for another person? In essence, we must begin giving back to ourselves and I will show you how in this chapter. The contents of this chapter can be applied at any point in the day to not only gain the benefits from a particular exercise, but to build trust and momentum in the health anxiety healing journey.

Not only do we want to add in self-care, we also want to recognize the habits that deplete our life force and continue to lead us toward catastrophic perceptions around our health.

It is very important to identify the junk foods and activities that will give you limited satisfaction and follow with a crash. These are the old habits we must replace. For example, sugar, caffeine, alcohol, and late-night partying (with or without alcohol) will give you good feelings in the moment, but the imbalance of blood sugar and circadian rhythm, or physical overexertion, is bound to wreak havoc on your emotional state and, over time, will make your health anxiety worse. When stress and anxious habits get bad enough, it is common to run from our thoughts and feelings by becoming obsessive about cleanliness, order, or work, leaving our self-care needs behind. Alternatively, a typical depressive state can cause someone to care less about the upkeep of their house or appearance. Everyone at one time in their lives has turned to food as a way of stuffing feelings down rather than dealing with them. We are not here to self-diagnose depression or anxiety just because your car is a mess or your house is sparkling clean. Instead, self-care is about recognizing where all of your focus and energy is currently going. It is necessary to recognize these patterns now and replace them with new empowering habits, to allow balance and flow back into your life!

Implementing the 333 Method

Self-care does not need to be fancy or expensive, and you should never feel guilty about taking time out of your day to take care of yourself. One of my favorite ways to implement self-care is with the "333 Method." This method ensures that every 3 hours you take 3 minutes to decompress, take mini-vacations away from whatever you are thinking of and doing, and recharge your emotional battery. This can be done by going for a 3-minute walk in nature, cultivating 3 minutes to focus on your breathing patterns, taking a 3-minute invigorating shower, walking 3 minutes in the grass barefoot, or 3 minutes to sip your tea distraction-free! Set an alarm on your phone or watch to go off every 3 hours (during the day). Implement the 333 Method for 3 weeks and it will have a positive effect on your health anxiety.

It takes at least 3 weeks (21 days) to create a new habit.

This is very effective when you are dealing with an onslaught of stress, fears, and anxiety. Over time, your emotional mind and body will begin to recognize the patterns being developed by the new habit and you will reap the benefits energetically, physically, and emotionally.

Dry Skin Brushing - The Ultimate Detoxification

Dry skin brushing is beneficial for detoxification of the lymphatic system. The lymphatic system is responsible for collecting and transporting waste to the blood. Dry brushing stimulates the lymphatic system and invigorates the skin, promotes cell rejuvenation, and removes toxic waste and lactic acid. Dry skin brushing helps improve blood circulation, digestion, and immunity. It is one of those rare things that feels good when you do it yourself and is incredibly easy to incorporate into your routine. I suggest doing it in the morning because it can be energizing for some. Do dry skin brushing 2-4 times per week for ultimate benefits. You will need a natural, medium-soft dry bristle brush with a long handle. To begin dry skin brushing, stand in the shower (this is just to catch dry skin that falls off). Start at your feet and brush upward toward your heart. When you move up and to your arms, follow the same flow, begin at your hands and work upward. Brush firmly, in a small circular motion. For the stomach and back area, brush in a counter-clockwise pattern. It should take approximately 4 minutes to brush your entire body. Once you are done brushing you can have a shower right away or go to a steam bath or sauna for extra detoxification.

Magnesium, Citrus, and Tea Baths to Relax & Revitalize

Magnesium baths have long been used to relax overworked and tight muscles. Magnesium hosts plenty of essential minerals that relieve insomnia, protect your heart, combat asthma, reduce high blood pressure, improve digestion, relieve constipation, and help stabilize blood sugar. Magnesium chloride is more easily absorbed into the body than Epsom salts, and can be found in most health stores. While both are wonderful for deep relaxation, the effects of magnesium chloride are much more intense. Magnesium typically comes from seawater and is often used for those people who have severe magnesium deficiencies. Magnesium chloride is not to be ingested—unless it is food grade—and is best absorbed through the skin. Implementing a relaxing magnesium bath before bed for a deep night's rest will contribute greatly to ending the mental chatter you may be succumbing to prior to sleeping. To begin, fill a bathtub with warm water. Add 2 cups of magnesium chloride flakes or 2 cups of Epsom salts. If you don't have a bathtub or simply have less time on your hands, fill a big bucket with warm water and add ¾ cup of either magnesium chloride flakes or Epsom salts and soak your feet for 15-30 minutes. If you really want to go all out, get creative and add a few drops of aromatherapy oil to your bath or foot soak (think lavender or peppermint) and add some candles for a super tranquil experience. Cayenne is a great spice to intensify the detoxification, however, I only recommend this in a foot soak rather than a full-body bath.

Tea Baths

Yes, you read that right; I want you to soak yourself in… herbal tea! This practice is highly regarded in homeopathic and holistic cancer treatment. Think chamomile, catnip, lemon balm, lavender, linden leaf, or any other relaxing herbal concoction. Absorbing tea through our largest organ, our skin, is incredibly therapeutic for health anxiety healing. To create this experience in your own home, add 5 tablespoons of your relaxing herb of choice to the bath water, let the tea steep for at least 10 minutes, and then hop in for a 20-minute soak.

Citrus Baths

There's no right or wrong way to throw yourself a citrus bath party, but this recipe for a relaxing lemon and lavender bath will get you started: Shake some sea salt into a tub and run hot water. Add lemon slices (from one lemon) to the tub as it fills with water. Add a few drops of lavender essential oil and sink in for a totally rejuvenating and relaxing bath.

Mindful Eating

"When practiced to its fullest, mindful eating turns a simple meal into a spiritual experience, giving us a deep appreciation of all that went into the meal's creation, as well as a deep understanding of the relationship between the food on our table, our own health, and our planet's health." — Thich Nhat Hanh

Remember how I mentioned that slowing down will have a very positive effect against health anxiety? Mindful eating goes hand in hand with the new speed of life you will be incorporating into your days to heal health anxiety. Indulging in self-care by getting a massage, getting your nails done, or reading a book is the first thing that comes to mind when we think about self-care. As great as these things are, the most important act of self-care is self-nourishment, both emotionally and physically. This is done by preparing fresh food and eating it mindfully. Mindful eating means focusing on what is on your plate. Multitasking while eating makes it difficult for you to listen to your body's hunger cues. Mindful eating helps you understand hunger signs, appreciate food, and prevent cravings and binge eating. So, the next time you sit down to have a meal, get rid of all the distractions (books/phone/TV/ laptop/music) and focus on the task at hand—eating! Take your time to see, smell, savor, and swallow every bite of your food. I am all about family gatherings around the table, but if you are by yourself don't even read a book; sit in silence and be grateful for the food you are eating.

The Art of Doing Nothing

I personally give myself permission to not feel motivated all the time. I used to think that motivation was a powerful flame of desire that would drive me to do what was good for me, no matter what. After all, if something was important enough, I should want to do it all the time, right? Not really. As time passed and I gained more experience in life, I came to realize that there will be highs and there will be lows in life. It's important to recognize these kinds of feelings and allow yourself to be in this place without feeling guilty about it. Give yourself the space you need to breathe and be still, and then, when you're ready, gradually start easing yourself into the steps you need to get yourself to where you want to be. Being hard on yourself is easy; loving yourself and accepting everything for what it is takes more effort, but is also a dangerously freeing way to live. The permission to 'do nothing' may seem boring, but this feeling of boredom is only a defense mechanism from the inner child warning you that you must stay busy in order to align with your core beliefs.

Give the inner child permission to do nothing, to feel unmotivated at times. A lack of motivation doesn't have to mean depression. Take into account that bodily and mental symptoms may be most active during these moments of downtime. This brings forth a challenge for you, doesn't it? You can see this as a practice opportunity or go back to 'distraction action'. If I were you right now, I would embrace these moments, since how you go through them will determine how long your health anxiety will stay around for.

Massage Yourself

Massage is one of the best ways to boost serotonin levels and reduce stress hormones. Giving yourself a massage can be just as beneficial as receiving one from someone else. There really is no wrong way to give yourself a massage, but here are a few tips if you need guidance. Beginning from your feet to your heart, massage your body, giving thanks to each muscle and limb for helping you with your tasks during the day as you go. For the top of the legs, hips, and back, incorporate a tennis ball. Lie down on a tennis ball and slowly move back and forth. This motion will act like a deep-tissue massage and is best done before you nod off to sleep. This type of self-massage, combined with some stretching and a cup of herbal tea an hour before bedtime, is a great way to set yourself up for a restful night's sleep.

Foot Reflexology

Reflexology is a science and an art. There are reflex areas in your feet that correspond to other parts of your body. Reflexology brings balance and homeostasis to the body without side effects. The deeply relaxing effect it causes enhances blood flow, aiding in detoxification of built-up lactic acid and mucous throughout the body. Reflexology is a wonderful physiological stress reliever bringing along with it a peaceful mind and a sense of tranquillity and well-being. Undergoing reflexology with a trained practitioner is a real treat and is often considered necessary for a wide range of emotional health concerns and during recovery.

Aromatherapy

The aromatic compounds in these recipes speak the language of health and restoration in your body. Aromatherapy will be a super sidekick in your recovery. I used to laugh when people said that during my health anxiety days until I really began to benefit from vetivert, lavender, and neroli essential oils. Vetivert is listed as a remedy for anxiety, stress, and ADHD. It is not extremely popular in Western culture, however many countries such as India and Indonesia use this versatile plant for a host of ailments. It has an amazing capability to settle the nervous system and calm the mind. I personally feel that vetivert is helpful with hyperventilation and deep breathing. In Ayurvedic medicine, vetivert is described as the "oil of tranquility" and is traditionally used for alleviating stress, anxiety, depression, insomnia, hysteria, trauma, and panic attacks. In ancient Chinese medicine, vetivert oil was also believed to calm and cool the body and mind, and also to stabilize emotions. For these reasons, it was sometimes used as a meditation aid. As a nervine, vetivert maintains nerve health and heals the damage done to nerves from shock, fear, and stress. For women, vetivert can also cool hot flashes and tame mood swings associated with PMS.

Next up we have lavender, a more well-known oil. Serotonin and neurotransmitters love this high-quality oil, and for this reason, it can be very calmative for individuals with health anxiety. Neroli oil is a citrusy essential oil that will help clear your head, purify the air, reduce stress, and induce a good night's sleep.

Massage Oil Recipe

In a small 100 ml glass bottle, add 2-4 drops vetivert oil, 4 drops lavender oil, and 4 drops neroli oil, top the remainder of the bottle with jojoba oil. Massage on wrists, temples, behind the ear, and under the nose.

Essential Oil Room Spray

In a 100 ml – 250 ml bottle, add 5 drops each of vetiver, lavender, and neroli, topped with filtered water. Spray around the room, on pillowcases, and clothes. Inhale, exhale.

Calming Diffuser Recipe

Add 2-4 drops of vetivert oil, 4 drops of lavender, and 4 drops of neroli. Add water to the diffuser. Enjoy! Be open to different aromatherapy scents. You might find mint to be extremely calming because it takes you back to a specific positive childhood memory, like your mom preparing you mint tea. I highly recommend giving plenty of aromatherapy oils a sniff for yourself to decide whether they feel calming or stimulating for you.

Essential Oil Precautions...

Vetivert, lavender, and neroli essential oils are non-toxic, non-irritating, and non-sensitizing. There are no known contraindications for mixing it with medications, but there is one big exception: Do not use vetivert if you are pregnant since it could cause miscarriage. (In some societies, it has been used for this purpose.) And since no studies have been done to test its safety on infants, it's best to avoid vetivert while breastfeeding.

Reflecting on Your Achievements & Acting on Your Goals

Reflecting on past significant achievements allows the brain to relive the experience positively. Our brain has trouble telling the difference between what is real and what is imagined, so it produces serotonin in both cases. This is another reason why gratitude practices are so popular; they remind us that we are valued and have much to value in life. If you need a serotonin boost during a stressful day, take a few moments to reflect on your past achievements and victories. Bring this practice into the present moment. How can you bring back those past achievements and feel-good moments into the present day? Write down a list of short-term and long-term goals and describe what you need to do each day to get closer to making those goals a reality.

Hugging & Laughing

Human-touch studies show that hugging can reveal emotions including anger, fear, disgust, love, gratitude, and sympathy, with accuracy rates of up to 83%. Hugs are one of the best ways to release oxytocin (yes, self-hugs included), and the more oxytocin you release, the better able you are to handle life stressors and boost both your mood and energy. Hugging is a beneficial way to create parasympathetic balance.

A good, hearty laugh relieves physical tension and stress, leaving your muscles feeling relaxed for up to 45 minutes afterward, and boosting your immune system. Laughter decreases stress hormones and increases immune cells and infection-fighting antibodies, which means better resistance to illness and disease. I know it might sound a little silly to have to schedule laughing, but in this day and age, it is necessary! Laughter therapy comes in many creative forms and can have a huge impact on your health anxiety recovery. Anyone who wants to re-experience the childhood feeling of freedom and bring looseness back into their lives can retrain himself or herself to laugh again. Laughter is transformative, invites playfulness, and can even be contagious.

Don't wait until your health anxiety is completely healed to laugh again. Laugh now so it contributes to healing health anxiety.

Many of the self care habits mentioned here will have a very positive effect on stimulating the vagus nerve. The vagus nerve represents the main component of the parasympathetic nervous system that oversees a vast array of crucial bodily functions including control of mood, immune response, digestion, and heart rate. The vagus nerve is found right behind where the pulse is found in the neck and is the longest nerve in the body. It's one of 12 cranial nerves and extends from the brainstem all the way to the abdomen and through various organs including the heart, esophagus, and lungs. Vagus nerve stimulation has the potential to contribute to healing not only health anxiety but also depression, PTSD, and bowel disparity. So, take it from me when I say that these self-care habits mentioned in this chapter must be a lifestyle act, not something you do once in a while to rid yourself of your mental chatter or physical symptoms.

Remember, these self-care habits will lead to the activation of your vagus nerve which will, in turn, activate the parasympathetic system, leading to rest and digest. When the rest and digest system is balanced out with the sympathetic system, everything begins to look safer than it used to, even your own anxiety symptoms. See your health anxiety healing as 'healing the whole'; the whole that represents all of you rather than focusing on just one aspect of the healing journey. Soon enough you'll look back and not even realize that you are no longer anxious toward your health, but rather excited for the change to come.

Please also keep in mind that reflection as to which techniques and self care routines from this book will contribute to your healing the most. Every person is unique and requires something different depending on where they are in their healing journey. Also, keep in mind that you mustn't ever gauge your progress based on whether your anxiety sensations are still present or not. If you do you will only grow more frustrated since the body is the last to catch up to the mental, behavioral, and other changes taking place for you right now. This is where your trust in the journey will be tested, so stay patience persistent, and with the end result vivid in your imagination and when the time is right it will happen.

Chapter 15:
Rebuilding Your Identity -
Creating The New You

One of the best questions I've ever received was from someone who was deeply confused about how the health anxiety healing process should go. The question was, 'Do we heal by breaking down the root causes of health anxiety, therefore taking steps to unravel ourselves from the health anxiety identity we've created? Or do we replace the identity first, therefore unraveling the root causes of health anxiety as it arises?" The answer to that question is either, or both.

This journey is one of self-exploration and of breaking down the walls of resistance when the time for change comes.

Some may find that they put their hearts into a method that regresses them to the causes of health anxiety, often stemming back to childhood and working forward from there. Others work backward from the present, mindfully creating disinterest in their unconsciously created fear-based identity and re-creating a new one. I'm a fan of both processes, therefore I place so much emphasis on reframing (regression work through somatic and imagery engagement) and responding (replacing the actions that lead to anxiety with actions that lead to emotional neutrality in the moment of anxiety sensitivity).

You have two main sets of identities at war within you: the one that you want and the one that you were programmed to have.

An identity is a filter that represents who you are and what you deserve. This filter acknowledges and approves of what fits within your identity and creates defense mechanisms for the things that don't. For example, a person who identifies with health anxiety will be emotionally committed to protecting themselves from physical illness and potential disease. A person who identifies with being an athlete will feel emotionally connected to sports and sort for connections to sports unconsciously within their environment. A person who identifies with being at peace will find peace in any situation, even within death itself.

Identity statements play one of the biggest roles in preserving and strengthening our identities. These are statements that begin with the words 'I am', as in 'I am a hypochondriac', or 'I am mentally ill'. What you need to understand is that the words that come after 'I am' are direct commands to your subconscious mind. They are taken very literally and pave the way for what your default way of feeling (and identity) becomes. However, replacing your self-sabotaging 'I am' statements with 'I am doing' statements takes the pressure off of your inner child to maintain an anxious state. For example, use the words "I am doing things that cause me to feel anxious' regularly and suddenly you feel less powerless and more in control of your behaviors and emotional state.

You can choose to identify with any or no self-labels whatsoever, the choice is always yours.

The identity you walk around with today is a result of years of external and unconsciously led internal conditioning. Now, you must begin identifying with whatever brings you a sense of inner peace and genuine pleasantness. Here are the stages of identity development from the old you to the re-creation of a new you:

Stage 1: Comfort zone – A familiar way of thinking about things and places we spend a large amount of time in. Our connection to our core beliefs, which began young.

Stage 2: Learning zone – A slightly challenging way of perceiving and reacting, along with places we physically spend time in. Here a person is introduced to a new experience that can provide a new perspective.

Stage 3: Challenging zone – Where most people go back to their comfort zone because it's too big of an investment and the emotional pain and discomfort is too much. The challenging zones are mental, emotional, and physical experiences where a person feels highly distant from their typical way of doing things and feeling.

Stage 4: Empowered zone – A manifestation of new ideas that have been strengthened through unfamiliar experiences. A new identity is well on its way as the old limiting habitual ways lose their power over the person.

Stage 5: Mastery zone – Where a person feels completely comfortable in their new mind, feelings, and actions. What can be controlled is fully controllable, and what can't be controlled is left to their higher power.

Where do you stand in your progression out of your old health anxiety identity and toward inner peace? Be honest, because without brutal honesty there are only lies, and aren't you tired of living a lie? We lie to ourselves each and every day when it comes to the potential of internal and external threats, never seeming to give ourselves the respect we deserve. Our minds can change the way they create associations, our bodies can heal things that leave the best physicians flabbergasted, and the spirit can renew its own life force projecting energy that positively affects everything it meets again. These are not lies, these are truths, and the ancients have been telling us this for centuries, but only the ones that have dedicated themselves to being their own healers will find this kind of wisdom.

Let's also mention a zone in stage 3 that commonly leads back to stage 1; we call this the panic zone. The panic zone (within the context of health anxiety) is a place where you step too far outside your comfort zone only to find yourself overwhelmed with bodily symptoms and catastrophic thinking. This usually happens out of impatience, as a person wants to skip steps and get right to the finish line quickly. Your healing journey is not meant to be this way, however, as the lessons you need to learn about both yourself and life lie within the very next step that demands your focus and energy. Like a car driving slowly in the dark only able to see a short distance ahead, you must also respect your journey enough to be true to it, and true to what your intuition says. Allow impatience to interfere and you will find yourself quickly back into looking for quick fixes. Start looking for quick fixes and you will negate all the work you have done. Instead, understand when it's time to push (challenge yourself) and when it's time to allow (letting the inner child process the last challenge you overcame). It is this balance that leads to empowerment and a whole new standard of values for yourself. Here are a set of questions that will challenge you to look beyond guilt and blame. Answer them honestly and with the knowledge that you can embrace any 'messy' feelings that arise by you challenging yourself:

Identity questionnaire – Who have I become? Count how many yeses you get:

1. Do you suffer from insecurity and low self-confidence?
2. Do you focus more on what you do wrong or what you fail at than on what you do right or well?
3. Do you feel less than or not as good as other people because you are not perfect at what you do or how you look?
4. Do you believe you need to do more, be more, and give more in order to earn the respect and love of other people?
5. Are you aware of having a critical inner voice that frequently tells you that you did something wrong?

6. Are you constantly critical of your performance at work, school, sports, etc?

7. Are you critical of the way you interact with others; for example, do you consistently kick yourself for saying the wrong thing, or for behaving in certain ways around others?

8. Do you feel like a failure in life, in your career, or in your relationships?

9. Do you identify with being a perfectionist?

10. Do you feel that you do not deserve good things, and do you have a sense of hesitation when good things happen?

If you answered yes to more than 5 questions you need to:

1. Understand **Where** your CORE beliefs came from.

2. Understand **Why** you hang onto them (possibly out of safety, consistently, fear of change, lack of belief in yourself, etc).

3. Understand **Who** is a role model who has the kind of self-worth and identity that you want to attain. Not ego, but self-worth and **Start** learning from them.

4. Begin learning and applying the skill of thinking and begin differentiating thinking from remembering/replaying.

These are the kinds of reflections we want to have. Reflecting takes a much broader viewpoint than analyzing, and unfortunately, the ones dealing with health anxiety over analyze too much while reflecting too little. Again, these points are not meant to take you to a place of guilt over the habits you are leaving behind once and for all. They are meant to open you up to the kinds of questions you need to ask yourself in order to start a brand-new relationship with your own inner child. One that doesn't lead to an identity based on what we were told to believe from when we were young, and one that isn't led by our 'failures' as a child. Better questions lead to better answers, so take your time right now. Notice how you feel after answering the questions you just have in this chapter. If you don't feel great about yourself, allow it to be there without adding to it because remember, you are allowed to feel whatever it is you are feeling. Practicing the art of not mentally adding to these feelings will eventually lead back to inner balance, which will eliminate the protectiveness we feel while holding onto a health anxiety-connected identity.

Once an idea is accepted in the inner mind it remains there until it is replaced with a new idea. Whenever we take something out we need to put something back in its place.

Whoever and whatever you identify with being right now in your life must be replaced, not eliminated. Too often when dealing with health anxiety we try to quit things like worrying for example, but worry is there because you unconsciously choose it to be there. It's a familiar source of protection for you and makes you feel protected by the illusory internal and external threats you've come to believe in. Where eliminating worry stops useless inner dialogue and self-advice, replacing worry has the potential to create a whole new outlook on life and a new identity along with it. Remember, when it comes to the components of health anxiety, anything that pulls you back into the cycle of worry must be replaced with something new. This means the internal thoughts and imagery, and the external words and behaviors.

Every suggestion that is accepted and acted upon makes the next suggestion more likely to be accepted and acted upon. Every time a suggestion is rejected it makes it more likely that the next suggestion will be rejected.

Keep this in mind, always. Fear grows and so does inner peace, depending on which suggestions are accepted and which are rejected. Accept that an anxiety symptom could potentially be an illness that is newly discovered and soon your body will be as anxious as your mind is. However, reject the idea and deem it as being one of the other 10,000 fleeting ideas you get daily and soon you'll find yourself more mindful of the idea that optimal health is your truth. As you become more aware of those initial moments of fear and take a stand against your old habitual ways of perceiving your bodily anxiety-led symptoms, you will find that fear begins to subside and as it does, you will find yourself in a different inner zone. In this place there is no need to label it as either good or bad, simply explore this new zone of defiance more deeply as your inner child turns from fear to self-love.

When dealing with the subconscious mind and its functions, the greater the conscious effort, the less the

unconscious responds. Trying too hard will resort to the unconscious wanting to run the show. Instead, develop positive mental expectancy that your problem can and will be solved.

In simpler terms, this point represents the idea of balance. Push through the conscious mind to turn an idea into a belief too soon and you will pay the price of succumbing to the inner child's fears once again. Yes, at the beginning of the healing journey there must be plenty of conscious attention and re-direction, but too much and all faith can be lost. 'Over-committing' can leave a person wondering when the results will show up. Instead, have the mental expectancy that the results WILL show up when they are meant to. This puts all forcefulness and hope aside and replaces these with balance and positive expectancy. Are you currently trying too hard in thinking that this extra push and over-commitment will manifest faster results? If so, this kind of habit only represents fear in a slightly different way. You fear that doing less, and at times allowing more, will lead to FOMO (fear of missing out). This cycle represents your perfectionist side, and it must be tamed and it must be replaced.

What the mind expects to happen tends to be realized.

What you expect to happen will happen, maybe not in the exact way you expected it to happen, but close enough. Expectation is a much more powerful signal than hope, remember that. Hoping for change still places you in a low vibration, expecting change places you in a higher vibration and is the key to using the law of attraction favorably. Expect the right knowledge to show up when the time is right, expect your creativity to shine through naturally in time, and expect healing to be present in any way it chooses.

When we can connect enough pain to having anxiety be a part of our identity, we will begin seeing it as behaviors and actions, not us, not our identity. Connect pain to a future with anxiety and you will match the emotional intensity needed to follow through with your healing work.

The more pain we associate with change, however, the less likely we will be to follow through daily on our promise to ourselves to put health anxiety behind us for good. Pleasure, on the other hand, is having a vision of the future you in the back of your mind each day. Pleasure toward the end goal and pain toward a life of worry will lead us to the answers we seek and the results we deserve.

Identity and inner child work are some of the most rewarding directions you will ever meet with. For myself, I found it quite awkward at first as I moved through the world being true to who I knew I was. My hatred for people turned to understanding and compassion, the frantic pace I thought life should be lived at turned to what felt like slow motion, and my self-talk turned from paying close attention to my 'mistakes' to paying close attention to my smallest 'wins' over irrational fear. Challenge your limiting identity at every opportunity you get. As mentioned earlier, when you set an intention to change your inner world your resolve will be tested. These mini-tests that you face from one day to the next must be met with cooperation, not anger or increased pressure. You may notice that you get a question from someone that goes 'how do you feel today?' Normally you answer this question by identifying with being dragged around by health anxiety as you speak the words of soreness, increased tension, and physical irritation. This time, however, you are reminded that this moment holds within it a great opportunity for change. Instead of playing that same old health anxiety record, you mention how your shift in mindset is contributing to taking small steps in the direction of being healed. Welcome to the wonderful world of change.

Each win contributes to bringing mindful awareness to the next opportunity for another win. Over time you create distance between yourself and the elements that used to lead to health anxiety. The fear starts to dissipate and as it does it feels as though you're living a completely different life. These are the moments you feel like you are going beyond anxiety. Beyond a present led by a traumatic past and into a present led by creatively creating the future. As these new feelings and experiences take place you must continue to be resilient in the face of oncoming fear. One 'test' after another, your resolve grows as you begin shedding the negative weight you've been carrying in your body for years. Allow the lightness of healing to come over you and the gratitude of your efforts to shine bright. You are more than anxiety, you are more than a life of health anxiety; be reminded of this daily.

Chapter 16:
Fear and Sacrifices

Health anxiety is just another form of fear. Therefore, if we heal health anxiety but do not re-integrate into a new identity, we will only find other ways of suffering from anxiety. Without sacrifice, there can be no change. So, are you ready to sacrifice your old habits for new ones? Your old life for a new one? If the answer to that question is an uncertain yes, then you have internal blocks that need to be removed and replaced. These are commonly connected to losing something or losing out on something. Let me provide you with a sacrifice that a past client had to make that connected to her own health anxiety healing…

Jamie grew up in a very strict religious home. Every 'bad' thing she did as a child (from the perspective of her parents) was shunned, and she was told that God would make life very hard for her in the future because of her actions. As the years went by, she lived with the belief system that feeling anger, fear, or sadness was bad and that she would be punished for feeling these feelings. Verbally, if she spoke her mind, or behaviorally if she acted in any way other than the way her parents wanted, she felt that she would be punished in the future in some way. Talk about anxiety, talk about tippy-toeing around life. I knew that logically telling Jamie that these beliefs were 'wrong' wouldn't do much to convince her. She was the one who had to conclude that there was a whole new way of seeing herself and life. So, I began asking her some important questions such as:

"What is important to you about healing your anxiety for good?"

This question gets the emotions running deep and pleasure toward change begins overtaking the fear of it. She answered, "I feel like I would live my life free from being tormented by my parents and God." Powerful, because now she's starting to see things she couldn't before. Then I repeated the first question again, asking:

"And what is important about no longer being tormented by God and your parents?"

She answered, "I feel I would give my own children the flexibility to figure things out by themselves, and I would be free to follow my own spiritual path."

Now we were really getting somewhere. Remember, when we hit those emotional hot buttons there's no turning back anymore. Jamie needed to decide for herself that she needed to let go of her parents' views for good, so I continued by asking the same question again …

"Tell me," I said, "What is important about giving your children the freedom to decide things on their own and follow your own spiritual path?"

She answered, "I would feel accomplished as a parent as well as genuinely connected to whatever religious or spiritual practices speak to my heart the most."

One other thing to notice in this conversation was how often I was echoing her own words back to her in order to build trust and rapport with Jamie. The greater the rapport, the more chance of her sharing deeply held information with me, and the better chance we had to do our future techniques without any unconscious resistance.

Aside from rapport and trust-building, Jamie mentioned to me that for the first time, possibly ever, she was starting to feel empowered and free to detach from the belief systems that were conditioned into her from her past. All I did was continue to ask the question, "What is important about having that?" repeatedly until she connected enough pain to not changing and enough pleasure to changing. She felt safe in her world of fear, and this translated into feeling a certain degree of safety with her anxiety symptoms. It kept her health anxiety alive since she never gave herself any flexibility and space to see things differently. She admitted that she felt like she was letting her parents down by divorcing her old religious upbringing. However, because she knew that this was solely a clever defense mechanism by the inner child looking to prevent any kind of change to what was familiar, she was able to replace her guilt with the satisfaction of what this change was about to bring to her.

The greater the sacrifice, the greater the uncertainty.

Until now I bet you never realized how much sacrifice it would take to heal anxiety (and health anxiety) for good. Core beliefs that lead to irrational ideas around fear, obsessive habits you engage in daily that maintain the illusion of safety, friends and family members that talk about other people often and bring drama (therefore anxiety) into your life, these are just a few of the many patterns we need to replace if we truly want change in our lives. Let's do an exercise right now ...

Bring to your attention the answers to each of the questions below and begin immediately to replace what you feel needs replacing:

Personal perceptions – What sort of perceptions do you hold over who you are?

Environments – Where do you spend an excessive amount of time that only contributes to your mental, emotional, and physical fatigue?

People – Which people must you begin separating from in order to begin reconnecting with more like-minded people? People that emotionally complement the chapter in your healing that you are currently in?

Religious or spiritual beliefs – Take note of whether these beliefs are helping or hindering your personal growth. Be true to yourself, what direction are you really being led in?

Food – What is your relationship with food? Do you need to sacrifice excess salt, sugar, or excess carbs and replace these with healthier options?

Career – Are you fulfilled in your current job, career, or business? If not, what sort of creative endeavor would you like to begin undertaking so that in time you can change careers and free up more time for your main priorities in life?

Entertainment – Must you sacrifice your obsessions over reality shows? Horror movies? Your TV or social media time in general?

Nature – What is your relationship with nature? Do you see your nature time as quality time or wasted time? Is it time to sacrifice your old beliefs for new ones around nature?

As you can see, we are approaching health anxiety healing not from the angle of healing bodily symptoms and deleting thoughts that spur on further anxiety; we are engaging in a mind, body, and spirit approach so that the domino effect will conclude with health anxiety healing as well. To care for your body is good, to obsess over your body is not good. Health anxiety healing is removing the obsession we have with survival and the body. We start seeing things as being connected to energy fields, rather than matter. These are good signs that you are leaving the old behind and embracing the new. Health anxiety is a set of patterns that have normalized to the point of deeply believing in the stories that we tell ourselves. We are now seeing this clearly. We are seeing the things that are holding us back, internal and external. This is what this journey is all about, the unfolding of information held onto closely by the inner child that is just now after all these years reaching the conscious mind. As more clarity arises through the epiphanies that we are met with from time to time, we get closer to our true purpose for this lifetime.

What the definition of purpose is depends on who you ask, therefore I don't believe I need to share with you my definition, but rather make it clear that you and only you can define what your purpose is.

As we let go, we are bringing in.

Do not think of what you are losing when you step out of old patterns and into the creation of new ones. But rather, make friends with the beautiful unknown. Often people going through health anxiety have a hard time letting go of their relationship with fear and the fear-led bodily symptoms that things may get worse for them. Worry and all its 'branches' seem like safety nets to a health anxiety sufferer. Yes, it is possible that out of surprise the subconscious mind body may make your symptoms worse at the start, but in time these feelings will subside as they always have. Your symptoms haven't killed you yet and they never will, however, they will take up a certain degree of your attention. That is, until you recognize that the attention you place on your symptoms could be placed on defying your fears instead. Worry begins to take a back seat, and this is a good sign. Symptom obsessiveness turns to a fleeting instance where you recognize that you are having the experience of an anxiety symptom and nothing more. Hmm, having the experience of an anxiety symptom, imagine taking on that mindset? This would lead to a wonderful sacrifice, the letting go of an unconscious need to be overtaken by a physical feeling.

As humans, we love to over-complicate things.

We think more about the consequences of change than we do about the benefits. Anxiety is there to prepare us for something, some sort of action the subconscious mind believes we need to take. Understand that there is always an underlying reason for what we feel. In order to understand what these reasons are you must sit with them and observe them rather than absorb them. You will begin making peace with the messages that come with your symptoms rather than looking for solutions to ridding them, which only strengthens them over time. Let us begin simplifying things, starting right now, by sacrificing unhelpful habits for good, no matter what the cost is that the inner child reminds us of. The inner child is always time traveling and never living in the present out of a desire to protect. Bless him or her for looking after us in this way. Health anxiety is a signal that some internal pattern needs your attention. Stay open to understanding what these patterns are and when your intuition reminds you of the defiant answer, act on it. Take a stand, an empowered stand, and one day you will only need to look back to see how far you've come.

Chapter 17:
Observing Trauma: Finding the Pattern

The more we search, the less we will find. Regression work done through mentally investigating which past experiences connect to progression toward an anxiety disorder or physical ailment will leave you frustrated and answerless. When people ask me what I do, I don't say I'm an anxiety coach, since that would bring up ideas of coping mechanisms for an emotional state the person is in. No, I go far beyond that, and I must if my work is to survive long after I am gone. My work is to treat physiological discomfort which has its roots in suppressed emotion. That's it. Sometimes there may be a very real physical issue at play, but most of the time it comes down to the imagination playing a big part in believing that there is or there will be physical illness in the future. For me the definition of trauma is the way in which neurology encodes an experience, not what the experience was. Therefore, my reframing practices (which you can find on my YouTube channel and online programs) are not altering what happened to you, but rather altering the perceptions of what happened to you since that was also an available option during those childhood time periods. Since you had no access to thinking and reflecting at the time, you were led by how you felt, and how you felt got stored alongside what you saw, heard, felt, tasted, or smelt during the moments of trauma.

Trauma must not be dealt with logically, similar to health anxiety. You can understand something logically but never get to the point where your dominant thoughts get the message.

Your dominant thoughts are not what you think they are. They aren't the ideas that float into your head, but rather, they are your memories, your core beliefs, and your lessons/perceptual filters that manifest as feelings. Feelings are the key to the kingdom in terms of healing health anxiety. We're not looking to think differently since thinking often doesn't change how we feel about something. We're looking to affect change at a physiological level so that everything underneath this umbrella becomes affected as well. This is one of the biggest reasons I have a problem with today's first line of treatments, mainly talk therapy. Talk therapy can give you a sense of making progress, but that temporary feeling of progress is often only connected to the familiarity and safety you feel while talking about your past. Just because someone understands and is empathetic toward you doesn't mean it can have the effect of changing your perceptions and ultimately the way you feel about what traumas need reframing. More than anything, just look at your results. If you're making progress within the method you are using then good, keep going. If you've been doing the same thing for the past few years and find yourself feeling like you're on a see-saw going between extreme positive and extreme negative emotional states, you probably have to either question the method or ask your own inner child why it fears change so much and what positives it gains by staying anxious.

When you stop trying to change things logically, you start observing. When you start observing, you start to see patterns emerge.

Pattern recognition is one of those vital keys to healing health anxiety and re-defining yourself. Most people can't see the patterns that are negatively affecting them because they've grown accustomed to bringing logic to every situation. Growing up, you probably heard the words 'be realistic' plenty of times. Being realistic when it comes to which career choice you choose pretty much means to stay within the bubble of your family and don't venture off to unfamiliar and more creative lands. In turn, we never take the time to allow ourselves to feel what it is like to live between fear and excitement, to find that middle ground where uncertainty and the unknown lie. I look to visit this state of being as often as I can now post health anxiety because from this place of trust you learn a lot about yourself and the world. So much of what we were taught was taught out of fear, and you must understand this deeply since those teachings are still being enacted by you, unconsciously. Life is not meant to be survived; it is meant to be experienced. And when you're caught up in bodily anxiety symptoms and catastrophic thinking patterns there is no way to experience the miracles around you in the present.

The law of cause and effect was what I gratefully discovered while being in that neutral emotional state.

Every cause has an effect, and every effect has a cause. No longer was I cursing the world and everything in it for my health anxiety, but rather I was beginning to open myself up to the principle of law and effect. The power to simply expand your awareness around this principle will do wonders for you because you will no longer live in a world where you think that things happen to you out of the blue. Nothing that happens in this world is random, nothing that happens to us is random. Rather, everything manifests around a set of universal laws and principles that translate into what we feel and experience in life.

We must also understand the principle of vibration in relation to trauma, which says nothing rests; everything moves, everything vibrates. So, what sort of frequencies would we be releasing into the world if we are still unknowingly carrying around the heaviness of trauma within our own bodies? Our external reality becomes shaped by the heaviness or lightness that we project through our own bodies as we tend to live life the same from one day to the next. If interested, you can look more deeply into these principles through the magical teachings of Hermes Trismegistus and the Emerald Tablet, and connect them to how you've manifested the inner world you move with daily in your own life. Some of the principles may be challenging to understand fully at first, but that's the beauty of letting go and allowing yourself to understand them more deeply over time.

You will attract into your life the things that are in harmony with your dominant thoughts, and your dominant thoughts were created between conception and the age of 5.

Important, deeply important. Therefore I remind people that have committed to doing affirmations work daily to do them in their native language, mostly unguided, and directed toward their inner child. Much of what we needed to say and needed to hear was in our native languages in those early years, so to provide those messages in a language that the inner child understands most deeply is essential to reaching our goal of replacing fear associations with safety. It took me years to finally understand the power of this, and once I did, I began speaking to my inner child in Turkish and no longer in English. I had much more difficulty finding the words at the beginning because they were so foreign, I never heard them, nor did I say them! But these were the necessary dialogues I needed to engage in daily until I felt- key word, 'felt'- like things were changing. Having not heard the words 'you are appreciated' or 'you are safe in this world' can be highly traumatic in themselves. Understand that as much as we may think of trauma as being experiences that overwhelmed our systems, they were also verbal communications that were rarely or never communicated. Traumatic interpretations form the blueprint for life and pave the pathway for either genuine peace or anxiety. One or the other becomes our default mode in terms of how we perceive and operate in all situations we encounter.

Emotional trauma creates altered fear circuits in the brain.

One of the most challenging things for highly traumatized people is to confront their shame about the way they behaved during the traumatic episode. They stay traumatized to this day over what they did or did not do in those circumstances, and this leaves them feeling emotionally numb many times (a common symptom of trauma). Within shamanic practices, this numbness is considered 'soul loss', where parts of the soul have been left behind and scattered over time. Soul retrieval, however, would be the shamanic practice of calling back these soul parts to integrate back into the spirit today. What we must stay aware of as well is how trauma changes perceptions and imagination. Is your perception truly coming from the you that considers all perspectives? Or is it the result of a past traumatizing experience that is now only allowing you to see what it wants you to see? It's an important question. Am I seeing the whole picture here regarding what I fear the most? Or is my inner child filtering in the fear and filtering out the safety? Health anxiety sufferers imagine a near future that is fatal many times, which only fuels their need to 'stand guard' to every bodily sensation that feels off. Often, though, different isn't all that bad. Yes, it may feel different, but maybe it's the body's way of digesting food, repairing muscles broken down during exercise, or healing a wound. The sounds and feelings are often healing processes but, unfortunately, health anxiety makes us believe otherwise.

Storing trauma is a lot like the Ghostbusters movie. However, instead of zapping and storing ghosts in a small box before putting them into a bigger box, the nervous system zaps all data that is available during the trauma and stores it in the body for later access.

Some may think, 'why does the organism store all this information for later access?' For safety purposes, of course, since re-learning things repeatedly wouldn't be an optimal option. Once trauma happens, everything from the color of mommy's hair to the construction sounds outside, to the windy air conditioner blowing in your face, to the peanut butter still digesting in your stomach, to the smells in the room, is recorded by the system and all become future threats. The only difference is the emotional intensity and recurrence. A high level of emotional intensity means deeper storage within the subconscious mind. We attract into our lives whatever we hold deeply within us. If your subconscious mind is free of trauma, your conscious intentions can more effortlessly come to manifestation. However, if the encoded traumatic experiences are not assessed and reframed, there is a high likelihood that even the definition of love becomes backward. Every time we get in a relationship looking for love we find disagreement, punishment, and confrontation. Why is that, we wonder? Why is it that we get the same conclusion even in the presence of different people? Simply, though the person may look different, you've continued to attract into your life the vibration of your greatest desire, which is love, and in this case, love means conflict because of what you experienced at those early ages prior to your moral reasoning kicking in. Any external occurrence in your life is initially brought on due to the beliefs within the subconscious mind, remember that. Traumatic dissociation is what many health anxiety sufferers today experience as depersonalization and dizziness. We are meant to survive traumatic dissociation until a time comes when we learn to create new associations with past events and show the inner child that the world is a safe place to live in. I used to think that I would never get rid of this symptom of feeling overwhelmed. The swaying feeling, the lack of short-term memory, the feeling of living in a bubble, the imbalance; it was all extremely overwhelming for quite some time. However, when I began to regain the power I felt I had lost, re-focusing my attention from what could go wrong to what could go right, and feeling a genuine sense of safety in unfamiliar situations, this symptom wore off.

Bringing safety back into the body through touch and sound.

Think of traumatic dissociation (depersonalization) as an opportunity to see things fresh all over again. Like teaching a new puppy right from wrong upon bringing the puppy home, we must use a similar approach to reteaching our own inner child what's truly safe and what is not. Firstly, it's important when using touch that you describe to yourself in detail what it is you are touching or holding. Grab an apple, place it in your hand, and take notice of the things you would normally just rush through from day to day. What kind of inner feeling does the apple give you when you hold it? Does it feel hard or squishy to you? What are the intricate details of the apple that you never noticed before? Reconnecting by touch is vitally important in eliminating the symptoms of depersonalization and should be engaged alongside your childhood reframing work. This kind of mindful attention is an excellent 'pattern break' that will help you slow down and stop you from rushing to what is next on your to-do list. Next, take a walk in nature. Touch the trees, spend time with the trees, even verbally or just mentally communicating with them. Notice the details within the tree that you never noticed before and more will be shown to you. Next, place your hand in the flowing river of water and notice how refreshing it feels. As often as you can, use reflective touch as a tool to break out of an anxiety state and support your trauma healing work. Each time you create a new association for what the external things really mean, you are taking one more giant step toward safety perceptions within the world you live in. This has a direct effect on how you see everything, since we now understand what kind of power our feelings hold in interpreting everything within the immediate environment.

Sound also plays an important role in supplementing traumatic dissociation healing. Close your eyes while sitting at home, on a park bench, within nature, anywhere where you can let go and simplify your experience. As you close your eyes, mentally listen to or make the sound of healing that feels right to you. Some people imagine the sound of an angel singing at a high pitch and are whisked away to a place of great inner peace. Others will use the sound of 'ohm' and hum for an extended period as their whole body vibrates in unison and calm. Mentally or verbally create the sound of healing that fits you the best. I used to use sound as a very powerful healing tool with my own personal clients and within my workshops. We would commonly use a new sound while imagining an environment from the past that had a traumatic connection to it. The new sound of healing and peace in that exact environment made it possible to imaginatively spend time in that environment without a sense of being overwhelmed by fear.

Trauma can live within us for as long as we let it. Generational and personal trauma have the potential to lead us toward a life of fear, often unknowingly to the sufferer. However, I'm a big believer that the moment we begin living in a greater state of awareness and are no longer dragged around by the inner child's perceptions of fear, we begin to take back our lost power. In this state of being, we have the potential to see even our family's tragic past from a different angle, a different light. The possibilities are limitless, in fact. What I do know for sure is this; that by reading and implementing the teachings within this book you are not only leading your own life toward inner peace but also those of those that come after you. Future generations will one day look back and wonder as to who was the one that stepped out of the loophole of fear and trauma and led a 'different' kind of life, and yes, they will be referring to you and your tremendous courage.

Chapter 18:
Personal Health Anxiety Stories

Through these 3 short and personal health anxiety stories, I hope to open your mind up to what's possible. In each story you'll notice one commonality—I didn't die. During the rising of anxiousness and at the peak of each experience I thought I would have for sure, I told myself, "this time it's different," but it never was. The first experience led me straight toward a panic attack, in the second one I felt a heightened state of anxiousness but not panic, and the third one was simply a lingering feeling of anxiousness over a symptom that I was obsessive over. These stories represent the health anxiety scenarios that many people find themselves stuck in regularly. I'm sure you will be able to relate to these stories as well as find commonalities within them all.

Story #1) The fear of facing the day.

One early sunny morning I found myself awake and ready to go through my morning to-dos before heading off to work (work was tennis coaching back in those anxious days). The first 30 seconds upon waking up I found myself thoughtless and in an unfamiliar state. It was a blank feeling, no thoughts, no obsessions, and quite peaceful, in fact. However, after those initial 30 seconds had passed, I consciously reminded myself of what sort of state of mind

261

was most familiar and came with a sense of certainty, the one that worried over what my body was feeling. I turned my attention to whether the bodily symptom of dizziness was present, and sure enough, it was. As I was brought back to being hyper-focused on it, I felt a combination of being at ease because I was back in touch with who I thought I needed to be (anxious) and also frustration that the symptom was still there even after a good night's sleep.

What you must understand about me back in those days was that I only looked for quick fixes. I didn't feel I had time for structure, a plan, or anything that would take up too much of my time and energy.

As I stepped into the shower that morning, I felt my anxiety start to grow as I entertained ideas around brain tumors and potential cancer. I began replaying similar ideas from my past few weeks, months, and years that included catastrophic endings to a symptom. After the shower was done, I couldn't remember if I had even soaped myself or not, even though I had just gotten out of the shower. "Was this another sign of an impending illness?" I wondered. Quickly one idea connected to the next as I began having breakfast. I ate but didn't bother tasting my food, I had a cup of tea but didn't remember what it smelled like, I was completely focused on where these bodily symptoms were eventually taking me. I was scared, angry, confused, sad, and guilt-ridden, all at the same time. I knew that early that afternoon I would need a nap after allowing this much focus and energy to be put into the obsessiveness over my symptoms. However, was the nap out of tiredness, or was it a clever defense mechanism by the inner child to get me back into what it deemed was a safe place, my bed? That is up for discussion, though I personally believe it's a bit of both. With breakfast completed, I dragged my anxious and exhausted self into my car, ready to head to work. I was beginning to transition from being anxious to feeling panic and I felt it within my mind and body.

As I began driving to work I realized that I was going to be an hour and a half early. I wasn't even in tune with what time it was. However, because of the habit of getting to work extremely early and spending an excessive amount of time in my car before starting my workday negotiating with my body, I was unconsciously led to repeating past patterns. I began unconsciously imagining what my workday would look like, running back and forth between the bathroom and the teaching court in a frenzy. I could see myself getting dizzier by the minute, and I knew that my imagination would lead me directly toward manifesting what I had imagined. I knew I couldn't work in the state I was in, I may get fired, get laughed at, heck, I could potentially be the laughing stock of the entire country! I drove directly to the emergency room instead and in a panic, I parked my car right in front. I didn't care if it got towed or not, this was my life on the line, or so I thought. I rushed in letting the nurses know of my dire situation. However, as was the case in my previous emergency room visits, I had to wait in the waiting room. Luckily for me, there weren't many people waiting (I unconsciously knew there wouldn't be since the afternoon time was a busier time to visit). The next 15 minutes felt like 15 hours as I struggled to sit still. I went outside for some fresh air as I noticed myself getting even dizzier. As air hunger started kicking in I held onto the handrails and made my way back inside only to hear the name 'Dennis Simsek' be called. I made it to the desk with the jelliest of legs and a heart that felt like it was going to burst right out of my chest. After giving my personal information as best I could I was told to wait on a hospital bed inside for the doctor to come to visit me.

Fast forward: After an ECG, blood pressure check, head scan, and blood work were all completed nothing life-threatening was identified … Again.

I left the emergency room feeling defeated and relieved. Defeated, because I almost wanted them to find something wrong with me so that I could take care of it and not have to relive the experience over again. Relieved, because I truly loved life and wanted so badly to live a long and healthy life experience. My car was towed, as I knew it would be, and I had over 30 text messages on my phone from work wondering where I was. I had let my boss, my co-workers, and my clients down, again. But I was alive, and that was a plus. It was becoming a bit of a habit for me not to show up to work and give an excuse of being sick. I guess I was pretty good at what I did because they never fired me. I felt a sense of relief move through me as I began the long walk to the local tow company to retrieve my car. I reflected on my anxious morning and even though my dizziness was still present, I wasn't afraid of it, nor did I add to it since I got the reassurance I needed from the hospital. I thought to myself...

"How could a person feel the same feelings and sensations and have two completely different reactions and relationships toward it?"

It was a pleasant walk as I felt a weight lift off me. There wasn't any more anxiousness or panic, I was tired though, very tired, but also at peace. Those initial moments after reassurance has been gathered tend to bring much relief to the mind and body, however, it can easily become a habit we seek each time we become obsessed with our bodily symptoms, and that is not a good habit to build. I finally made it to the towing company and picked up my car. They asked me what I was thinking, leaving my car parked in front of the hospital like that. I replied, "I thought I was dying, again." I didn't expect them to understand, because no one really did unless they themselves had gone through health anxiety the way I had.

As I drove back home taking the day off from work, I naturally drove slowly, mindfully, and sensibly. I couldn't believe how just a few hours could make such a difference in my mental and emotional state. I went straight to my bedroom and lay down, reflecting on what just happened. It felt like a whirlwind of events, it all happened so quickly that it was very much like watching myself in a movie. I closed my eyes and fell asleep a few moments later. I had survived, but to me, just barely.

Story #2) To gather or not to gather?

It was Wednesday morning, and I was just invited to a social get-together. The gathering was at a local restaurant/pub, there would be alcohol involved (which never went well with my health anxiety), and there would be nowhere to hide for me and my anxiety. The gathering was to happen on that Saturday evening and upon receiving the invitation a few thoughts began to cross my mind ...

- What excuse could I have readily available just in case I felt overwhelmed?
- Which people did I have to distance myself from that night so I didn't get 'triggered'?
- Was there an alcoholic beverage that could calm me in case I felt overwhelmed?
- Would the focus on my bodily symptoms take over my conversations with others?
- Would I be made fun of?
- Would I never be invited to another get-together?

The list went on. You must understand that my health anxiety and other disorders commonly went hand in hand. For a few years, it was accompanied by panic, after that it was accompanied by generalized and situational anxiety, then agoraphobia made an appearance, and OCD was there throughout the whole thing, really. It wasn't until I was on the true path of inner healing that my heath anxiety was by its lonesome self and I had more influence over my bodily perceptions.

I accepted the request to go and found myself obsessing over how it would go for the next few days. You must understand, during those years worry was a part of who I believed I needed to be. Without worry in my life, I would feel naked and vulnerable. However, later on in the journey, I realized that it was vulnerability that held the key to my inner peace.

As Saturday evening approached, I couldn't stop touching myself, and touching my symptoms in the hopes that they would subside.

If a stranger saw me that evening I guarantee they would think that I was having a heart attack. The body zaps, the twitching in my arms, and the chest discomfort were almost too much to bear. I did bear these feelings, however, and walked into the restaurant 50% focused on my body, 40% focused on all the potential threats within the restaurant, and 10% focused on the fact that this could potentially be a victory of sorts. I wasn't in full panic mode, though I was anxious. The interpretation of the feeling was determined by what part of the experience I focused on most. Since I was so used to focusing on what could go wrong, I defaulted to it regularly. However, just the consideration that a new approach could be present was a dim moment of hope for the future.

Walking into the gathering I found my table and saw many familiar faces. I was greeted by everyone and had a choice to make: Was I going to be led by fear or something different this time? Fear prevailed, unfortunately. But again, lingering deep within me was the potential of bringing forth someone new. As the night progressed I was mainly looking to avoid interactions and continue to sip my tonic water (which others thought was gin and tonic, clever, I know). Back then cell phones weren't as popular as they are today so I didn't have the option of using it as a cover. Instead, I made multiple trips to the bathroom throughout the night because anxiousness can make you a peeing machine and it provided the opportunity to 'gather myself'. Another clever defense to a potentially overwhelming and new situation by the inner child? I believe there was, but to what degree is up for discussion. After all was said and done, I found that I had endured the night, survived the onslaught of bodily symptoms, and even had multiple 'wins'. I had sporadic conversations with others, I allowed rather than forced my symptoms to go away at times, and I followed through all the way until the end of the night without leaving. More often than not, when a health anxiety sufferer has this kind of unfamiliar experience they will spend the next few days analyzing each and every aspect of the experience to look for ways they might have messed up or made mistakes. However, at some point in this journey, we must stop analyzing and start reflecting on our 'wins'.

Momentum, either negative or positive, paves the way for who we become in the future.

What this means in its simplest terms is that the habits you install into your day will determine how you perceive yourself and your future experiences. Focusing on the wins generates a feeling of progress, and that feeling of progress will lead to spontaneous epiphanies throughout the day. These epiphanies are learning lessons that must be written down and studied in greater detail, since they are the very messages that take us from where we are to the next step on the ladder of healing.

I went to bed that night feeling like I was torn between thinking of my personal successes and failures. The choice was up to me, no one else. I needed to place the meaning I wanted on that night's experience, and I had to make sure it was the type of meaning that kept me on the path of healing. I decided to call the night a success and slept well that night. I woke up with challenging symptoms, yes, but I found that my mind wasn't as obsessed over them as I normally was. Remember, the feeling states you go to bed with will have a great effect on the next day. So focus is on the progress you made and soon you will find that you are making the transition from perceiving things fearfully to more neutrally, and then safely.

Story #3) Home sweet home?

Story number 3 takes place in my old environmental comfort zone, strangely enough, within the safety of my own house. Let us not think that just because we are in the presence of an environmental comfort zone that we will not dive into a cycle of worry concerning the catastrophic potentials of our bodies. It happens, maybe not as often as being in unfamiliar environments, but it still happens.

As I lay down watching TV one Sunday afternoon in my home, I found myself slowly but surely moving toward 'what if' possibilities based around the discomfort I was feeling in my body. Now understand this, health anxiety and panic can be brought on by lingering symptoms or sudden symptoms. The lingering kinds involve feelings like dizziness, a lump in the throat feeling, or jelly legs. The sudden ones can be things like chest pressure, head pressure, or a tingling in any part of the body. To a health anxiety sufferer, either kind can lead to a state of panic and overwhelm, or can even lead to a state of over-worry without panic. Either way, it's not fun.

In this case, however, my attention was drawn toward the increasing pressure in my chest. At that very moment, I certainly didn't think this is just the result of an increase in fear being justified by the inner child based on memory and core beliefs. No, I thought, 'why is this here, why doesn't it go away, and what will I do if the worst comes over me?' As one irrational thought connected to another, I found myself face to face with the over 50 different herbs, pills, and vitamins that I had in my closet, looking for an answer. In this instance, I didn't respond consciously but rather reacted unconsciously. Responding would be to place a new meaning over the feeling, use a pattern interruption to stop the progression of irrational thought and protective feeling, or even ask it to be present if it chooses as I refocus my attention back onto what I was watching on the TV. Reacting, on the other hand, was looking for a quick fix, replaying similar meanings from the past, or running to Google or a 'safety' person. During this time I had a short stint with a Benzodiazepine commonly known as Ativan (Clonazepam). This chemical worked quickly and was effective, but had addiction written all over it. I took half of what was recommended to me and waited for the chest pressure to pass, but it didn't do the job I had expected it to. So I took another half, and then another, and finally another. By this time I was slurring my words and felt like I had little to no control over my physical movements. The chest pressure was still there as a lingering feeling and I was on cloud 9 (good or bad was up for interpretation). I had replaced one problem (chest pressure) with another, since the next day after taking these pills I was certainly not functioning optimally. Not only that, there was the fear of over-toxicity in the body that I had read somewhere at the time that freaked me out, as well as the fact that my hope for long-term healing was starting to fade quickly.

Unconsciously, 'the pill' looked like the solution. Intuitively, however, I felt that the pill would lead to other problems long term.

There is, of course, a time and place for such medications, this I believe. However, my relationship with them wasn't one that would lead to any of the internal 'wins' I needed to heal. I started walking around my home dazed and confused, and still strangely anxious. As time went by I started to slowly come to understand how my perceptions truly affected my body. I realized that I was only dealing with thoughts that I wouldn't be able to function the next day, of internal toxicity issues, and of an inability to heal long-term. These ideas were made more real to me due to emotional attachment to them as well as the behaviors that rationalized that they were true, but none of it was. I met with a vital turning point that night, something I had known for a while but never understood to the level I had that evening. It was like a smack in the face saying 'get your perceptions together already, and stop falling for the ones that play out like a record player day after day'. I began to realize the power I had within me to create my own thoughts about things, my own actions, and my own outlook on my future. I knew that in those moments that I had the power to create my thoughts consciously instead of predicting them unconsciously, and that once a seed such as this was planted all I had to do was continue to act on it until it became the new inner program.

I'm not sure how or why these epiphanies came to me that night, but I do know that it was just a matter of time before I had more moments like that which would turn things around.

I began seeing my own brain from the perspective of a supercomputer that was running similar software programs from day to day. I needed an upgrade in software, and I didn't need it fast. What I needed was to stick to my intention, which was to begin changing things from the inside out rather than look to cope from the outside in.

Here we have 3 different types of health anxiety-related personal stories, each very common experiences between myself and others. Through the teachings centered around health anxiety healing, we have the opportunity to fall right back in love with ourselves again. Every new idea, every body part, every systematic function that works effortlessly within us, can be loved and appreciated all over again. This is the kind of love that gradually increases in strength over time. Soon you may find yourself smiling randomly while others wonder what's the reasoning behind your smile. No longer do such experiences feel like mistakes, however, because self-love has overtaken self-sabotage.

Chapter 19:
New Meanings

I have been where you are, my friends. I have been stuck in the clutches of fear for years only to find myself in optimal health afterward. As I look back, I realize that health anxiety gave me the opportunity to reinvent myself and get back in touch with the child side of me that missed out on a lot of his childhood (which may or may not be the case for you). My once rigid outlook has turned to flexibility and the need for control has turned to safety, giving up that need for something even better: trust. Whenever I need a word during my personal challenges these days I look to the word 'trust' to remind me that the way I feel about something and perceive something may not be true at all.

I've made it a habit to question my feelings about things and therefore I am no longer pulled toward bodily sensations being a potential threat to my life. This is my hope for you, this is where I believe you are headed. Motivation is a good starting point, but having the end result running in the background as a mental movie is what we must purvey to our inner child. I've realized that health anxiety is just another form of suffering, and if the identity doesn't change, nor will the pursuit by the subconscious mind to find a new way to suffer. I suffered through sports, through relationships, through financial affairs, and through a host of other things because my approach to life was that without struggle there can be no reward.

As young children we are told that we are good boys and girls only when a deed is done in the way the authority figure wants it done.

We were also told that we were bad boys and girls if we did something that was out of line with what the authority figure believed was right. Today, many of us continue to look to be good boys and girls, but in different forms. Does this feeling of tippy-toeing around people and life lead to some form of anxiety? You bet it does. Does it lead to further suppression? Absolutely. The moment we step out of our personal comfort zones and feel, say, do, or imagine something differently, we feel that we are stepping out of the lines that we were told to stay in by others. Again, we feel like bad boys and girls. Nonsense. You have all you need through this book and your own intuition to heal not only your health anxiety, but your whole perspective on yourself and life. The fear of tapping into that amount of power can potentially scare you more than anything, this I know to be true at the deeper levels. To find something new used to be a surprise when we were kids, nowadays anything new seems to be the most terrifying thing imaginable since we aren't sure of what connects to that new thing. We look for answers and yet seem to always come up with more questions. Questions that keep us mentally occupied and worrying. If you would, I would like you to do these 3 things right now to begin tapping into the power you hold within you…

1) With your eyes closed, imagine a black-colored balloon that is filled with air. Now slowly imagine the balloon deflating and listen to the sounds as it does. When the balloon is completely empty of any air, take a moment to notice how you feel.

2) With your eyes closed, imagine that you are holding a book very tightly and in that book are all the fears you feel in your body. Now, slowly begin to rip the pages out of that book and place them in the firepit next to you. One after another, rip each page, place that page in the fire and just keep going until the book no longer has any pages left. Once you are done, take a moment to notice how you feel.

3) With your eyes closed, notice that there is a big cloud above you in the color of your fear. Notice as well that you have a string on your hand connected to that cloud. Cut the string, release the cloud, and let it float away as you wave goodbye. Once the cloud is gone completely, take a moment to notice how you feel.

Remember, color, sound, and vibration, these are the types of languages that convince the inner child that it's safe to let go of the fear and the safety net we have come to know as being worried. I hope that these 3 imagery-based skill sets showed you just how quickly change can arise in your life, and, yes, you can use them along with your reframing and responding skill sets you learned through this book (and will continue to learn through my programs and YouTube channel). Keep it simple going forward; if a technique speaks to you, use it. If it doesn't, use something else. There is no rule in the health anxiety healing world that says your recovery must follow an exact process. This is a feeling out journey more than anything. The lessons from one 'win' will take you to your next challenge and your next 'win', and so on until you get to the point where you understand why you had to go through health anxiety the way you did. At this point these words may feel foreign to you, but remember to trust. Trust in the process of healing because you were brought to read this book for a specific purpose, this I believe fully. Your light will be shining brightly into the world soon but you must be patient. You are the vibration that will affect everything in this world in a positive way, but first you must be willing to unlearn what needs unlearning.

Health anxiety healing is both the end of suffering and the beginning of allowing.

To allow is to trust, to trust is to have faith. You are now the driver of your own bus, the captain of your own ship, the pilot of your own plane. You have full permission from your own subconscious mind/inner child to allow the parts of you that you've suppressed for far too long to come out and join your life experience. As you fear failure less, you will fear your symptoms less as well, and as you find comfort in uncertainty you will release yourself from the need for reassurance over your healing. As you step into the unknown with trust, so too will you step out of needing to know the answer to each and every bodily symptom. As one domino falls so will the next within the time frame that it needs to. As you allow the process of healing to unfold, you are allowing the process of co-creating your life experience to unfold. Source energy (or whatever it is you believe is accompanying you externally on this journey) will feel like it is always present with you. This is very comforting. So comforting, in fact, that you may even start fearing the process of death less and become intrigued by what may lie on the other side of this life.

Imagine that. When you begin fearing death less you can begin living the way you're meant to live more often. This I have found to be very true in my own life. Many think that the fear of death is the main perpetrator of health anxiety. However, as mentioned earlier I tend to believe that the fear of truly living a life outside of how we've been told to live and be is the greatest perpetrator of a life of suffering. When you can fully grasp this concept, the world will begin opening its arms up to you, I mean that. What you put out you will bring back in, which means that when your default way of feeling turns from fear to self-love your life experiences will match this change. This is the beauty of healing health anxiety.

Notice I didn't use the word 'coping'. Remember, words are direct commands to the inner child.

'Coping' translates into 'taking care of' and 'dealing with', but you don't want to take care of and constantly deal with your anxiety symptoms, do you? Of course not. Healing, on the other hand, means 'to move beyond'. Going forward, pay attention to the words you use in your inner dialogue since you converse with yourself more than any other person. Every word or sentence that is accompanied by a heightened state of feeling brings it that much faster toward becoming a core belief. Once an idea has turned into a core belief it acts like the bouncer at a nightclub. The bouncer will only let in the people (in this case the ideas) that fit the vibe of the club (core beliefs). Inner peace will be as automatic as your anxiety once was. I mean, how effortless was it to go into a state of anxiousness for you in the past? Effortless. Now imagine inner peace being that effortless, however, it does take practice to master a new state of feeling. You've consciously and unconsciously practiced being anxious on a daily basis until you got the feeling just right. Now, we're simply redirecting that level of focus and energy toward the opposite side of the scale. Your symptoms aren't a sign of impending illness or disease, rather they are a sign of fear. If you were on a first date and your date was afraid of a particular scene in a movie, you would comfort him or her, wouldn't you? You wouldn't go along with their interpretation of that scene, but rather you would gently bring them toward a place of safety. This is when the magic of healing health anxiety really gets moving. This is when you no longer succumb to an initial feeling but instead redirect the feeling toward a new meaning.

Change the meaning and you will change the feeling.

In the end, isn't that what all of this is about anyway? A change in meaning? Once we wholeheartedly believe that our fears mean something different, isn't that the beginning of the end of being dragged around by fear? I believe it is. Anxiety can now mean excitement, symptoms can now mean a message from the inner child, sleep debt, a meal missed, unresolved anger toward your ex, or loneliness even, anything but what it used to mean will drive you toward self-care rather than increasing your levels of anxiety. Once the new meanings have taken shape you will have an increased feeling of disinterest in the old meanings. Like throwing a piece of trash in the garbage can, how many times in your life have you gone back and looked to retrieve that piece of trash? Rarely, if ever, since it has no value to you anymore, or else you wouldn't have thrown it out. Just as the old fearful interpretations that you used to be consumed by, your health anxiety will lessen in value.

Anyone who believes that anxiety is a sign of weakness has never gone through it themselves because had they gone through it, they would know just how strong anxiety sufferers really are. Be comforted by your progress and your intention to create a whole new perspective over things you once feared. I believe in you. You're well on your way now, warrior.

Glossary

The processes and stages I outline in this book to guide you through your health anxiety healing will need you to dedicate both time and effort. As you go from chapter to chapter, you will see a number of words and terms come up again and again. The meaning of these important words are based on my own interpretations.

Take your time when reading. This glossary is here to be your reference guide and to remind you of the meanings of these words. They will help you understand the messages I am conveying.

Anxiety – A chronic psychological and physiological state of fear.

Associations – The connections held around what things mean and their level of safety versus threat, created either from the subconscious mind or conscious mind.

Bodily symptoms – Physical sensations that can appear anywhere at any time within the timeline of our lives.

Comfort zones – A familiar place of thinking, speaking, behaving, or imagining. A comfort zone can also be the types of people we surround ourselves with and places we spend time in. Like secondary gains, these can be both positive and negative; a waiting room may be a comfort zone even though this keeps us locked in a place of anxiety.

Consciousness – The level of conscious awareness from one moment to the next.

Conscious mind – The part of our brains that thinks and perceives from an experienced and updated point of view. Your calculated and determined reactions are the actions of your conscious mind.

Coping – A state of managing bodily symptoms and sense of being. This is opposite to a 'healing' approach that unconsciously feeds the need to keep this around because of the familiarity factor as well as the fear of what may happen if it leaves.

Core beliefs – The beliefs formed by the subconscious mind based on conditioning from childhood. These beliefs are used by your inner child to react and respond to your current everyday interactions.

Defense mechanisms – The mental and physiological reactions of the subconscious mind that look to deter you from taking action that would spur on some level of inner change.

Depersonalization – A common symptom of anxiety where the person feels detached from the world and experiences trouble focusing, memorizing, and even functioning through simple daily tasks.

Depression – A persistent depressive mood that doesn't change even when positives arise.

Enlightenment – The feeling of clarity, deeper intuitive understanding, and trust in the unfolding of life.

Epiphany – Spontaneous moments of deep clarity and understanding that lead toward new approaches or actions which, in turn, greatly contribute to the health anxiety healing journey.

Health anxiety – A form of anxiety that is obsessiveness over one's own health to the point of perceiving harmless bodily sensations and external information as real physical dangers to themselves.

Healing – A steady progression toward creating a new identity and moving away from the old conditioned identity plagued by our childhood perceptions and upbringing.

Homeostasis – A stable condition of physiological and chemical equilibrium.

Identity – Our self-concept. The idea we hold of ourselves that determines how we view who we are, what we deserve, how we fit into this world, and what we are capable and not capable of.

Inner child – The representation of our subconscious mind which manifests as initial feelings, and that which has connected safety to familiarity. Your instinctive, unconscious reactions are the actions of the inner child.

Intuition – A 'hunch' that comes from our heart sense, which is subtle.

Maladaptive techniques and habits – Actions that are temporarily beneficial for getting rid of a particular thought, symptom, or feeling at the cost of long-term benefits of adaptive techniques.

Mammalian brain (limbic system) – The part of our brains that connects emotions to an idea or immediate perception.

Mapping – A meditative practice of surrendering to the mind's interpretations and the sensations from the body.

Persona parts – Suppressed or expressed characteristics of a person based on the identity they identify themselves with.

Reframing – The practice of creating and of using different imagery to change the associations made in the subconscious mind for past and future events.

Reptile brain – The most ancient part of our brains, responsible for processing all sensory data first. The reptile brain has many functions but primarily its job is to protect, and prefers that you don't venture into new and unfamiliar experiences.

Repressed emotions – Consciously or unconsciously avoiding feelings and emotions out of a fear of re-experiencing them and being overwhelmed.

Responding – A conscious mental, verbal, behavioral, or imaginative response to a situation that spurs on some level of anxiousness.

Sacrifices – To let go of something in return for something else. Often during the health anxiety healing journey this connects to the letting go of ideas, identity, people, surroundings, and daily habits in favor of a more long-term and fulfilling reward.

Secondary gains – The unconscious motivation to do something in order to receive something. The subconscious mind feels like this anxious state comes with a reward from others and, in turn, likes to keep this steady run of anxiety alive since it provides something that may not be there should the person change. Secondary gains can have both positive and negative motivations; it seeks a position of familiarity.

Setback – An experience that is perceived as having taken steps backward on the path toward healing health anxiety.

Subconscious mind – Our infinite storage system that has unconsciously created the blueprint for who we are and what the world is. Often, when I refer to the subconscious mind I'm also referring to the body, as this is where our traumas and core beliefs get stored and becomes more evident over time.

Support system – The people in your life that you identify with as being your supporters on your path towards healing health anxiety.

Suppressed emotions – The act and result of consciously stopping and holding yourself back from feeling or thinking something.

Survival mode – A highly sensitized mental and physiological state wherein the person feels threatened to lose something that is dear to them throughout most of the day.

Trauma – An experience of overwhelm (often from childhood) coupled with a high degree of emotional intensity that becomes the association that the person lives with into their adult years. In this book, trauma refers to how the experience and external data coming from the senses were originally recorded and stored by your childhood mind. It is not based on what the experience actually was, it is more about how the experience was recorded. The legacy of this experience endures stronger than what actually took place.

Unconscious mind – The conditioned reactions stemming from the subconscious mind. The unconscious mind is the toolkit used by the inner child to determine their response to situations, meaning it uses past traumas to respond to present situations.

Victimhood – A state of feeling sorry for ourselves.

Made in United States
North Haven, CT
26 January 2024

47941432R00174